The Mitchell Beazley Pocket Guide to

Rocks, Minerals and Gemstones

Sue Rigby

This book is dedicated to my parents

Author's acknowledgement
Thanks to my father, Brian Rigby, a geologist and mineral
collector, whose help was so valuable in writing this book

Edited and designed by Mitchell Beazley International Ltd
Michelin House, 81 Fulham Road, London SW3 6RB

Editor: Marek Walisiewicz
Art Editor: Paul Drayson
Production: Sarah Schuman
Typesetter: Kerri Hinchon
Executive Editor: Robin Rees

Rocks and minerals photographed by Sally Cushing. Gemstones
photographed by Robert J. Reekie. Illustrations by Jon Rogers, Ian
Fleming and Associates.

A CIP catalogue record for this book is available from the British
Library

ISBN 0 85533 865 2

Typeset in Sabon
Linotronic output by The Imaging Business, London N7
Reproduced by Mandarin Offset, Hong Kong
Produced by Mandarin Offset, Hong Kong
Printed and bound in Malaysia

Contents

Introduction

Collecting rocks and minerals is a fascinating hobby. The variety of colour and texture of these natural materials is astounding. Many are beautiful and highly precious; others are of great economic importance. All give a rare insight into the processes that formed our planet and that are shaping our landscape today.

This book is a beginner's guide to the identification of minerals, gems and rocks. It explains the features that allow identification to be made, and describes all the common types as well as a selection of unusual varieties. It assumes no previous knowledge of the subject, or of scientific principles. Technical terms are kept to a minimum, and always explained where they are first used.

Many people are content to collect rocks and minerals for their own sake, but they are far more interesting for what they can tell us about the Earth. This book puts rocks and minerals into a broader geological context by explaining the physical events that lead to their formation.

Rocks, minerals and the Earth

The first rocks and minerals formed as the uppermost layer of the Earth – the crust – began to solidify about 4,000 million years ago. At that time there was no water on the planet, no fully-developed atmosphere, and no life. Geological change since that time can be traced by following the formation of different rock types. Igneous rocks tell us about changing conditions deep within the planet, while sedimentary rocks record surface processes.

The surface of the Earth is made up of gigantic "plates" of solid crust and mantle material up to 170 km thick. These plates are not immobile, but are moving very slowly, riding on top of a more fluid layer (the mantle) beneath. When two plates collide, huge energies are released, manifesting themselves in volcanoes, earthquakes and the formation of mountain ranges. It is in these areas of collision that many new rocks and minerals form.

There are two main types of crust – oceanic and continental. Oceanic crust, which is found only below the surface of the oceans, has a simple, distinctive composition, and a similar density to the mantle. When sections of oceanic crust collide with each other, or with the continental crust, they are forced back into the mantle. The energy released melts the rock of which they are composed, which then cools, forming igneous rock.

The continental crust has a complicated composition and is too buoyant to sink back into the mantle. It too can melt, cool and solidify, but into a different suite of rocks and minerals to that formed from oceanic crust.

Rocks derived from either type of crust may be altered by heat and pressure, or by surface processes, into an enormous array of rock and minerals. The illustration on pages 6–7 shows some of the ways in which different rock and mineral types form. Fuller accounts are given in the introductions to the book's major sections.

Collecting rocks and minerals

Many environments offer fertile ground for the collector. Quarries, beaches, cliffs, old mine workings and spoil heaps are often good sources. A geological hammer and cold steel chisel are useful tools, although fine specimens can be picked up from loose pebbles or rock fragments. All specimens collected should be carefully wrapped in paper or cloth to protect them from damage during transport. They should be clearly labelled with the location in which they were found: this may be useful to an expert should you have difficulty identifying the specimen yourself.

It should be remembered that the supply of minerals is not inexhaustible, so take as few specimens as possible. Specimens should never be removed from Sites of Special Scientific Interest (SSSIs), as these are areas of particular value and generally small in extent.

A code for collectors

As so much collecting is carried out in potentially dangerous situations, a simple code for geological field work has been devised by the Geologists' Association. Following the code is essential if good relations with landowners and site managers are to be maintained.

1. Follow the countryside code. Close gates and leave no litter.

2. Seek permission before entering private land.

3. Don't interfere with machinery.

4. Don't leave rock litter lying on roads and fields where it might be hazardous to humans or livestock.

5. Avoid undue disturbance to wildlife.

6. On coastal sections, consult the local Coastguard Service whenever possible to learn of local hazards such as unstable cliffs and tides.

7. When working in mountains or remote areas, follow the advice given in the pamphlet *Mountain Safety* issued by the Central Council for Physical Education. Always inform someone of your intended route.

8. When exploring underground, be sure you have the proper equipment and necessary experience. Never go alone. Inform someone of your departure, location, estimated time underground, and return.

9. Don't take risks on insecure cliffs or rock faces. Take care not to dislodge rock, since other people may be below.

10. Be considerate. By your actions in collecting, do not render an exposure untidy or dangerous.

Further advice can be obtained from The Geologists' Association, Burlington House, Piccadilly, London W1V 9AG.

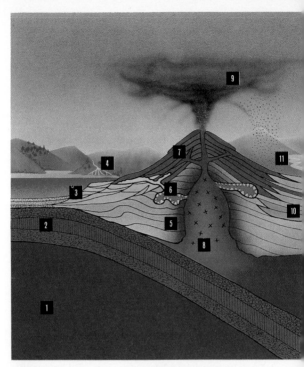

| Igneous rocks | Metamorphic rocks |

This generalized cross section through the Earth's crust and upper mantle shows the common sites of rock and mineral formation

1   The Earth's mantle lies immediately under the crust. It begins between 6 and 70 km below the surface and extends to a depth around 3,000 km. When partially melted it forms magma, the raw material for igneous rocks

2   The oceanic crust descends into the mantle and partially melts. The magma rises through the crust to produce volcanoes

3   Biological and chemical processes deposit limestone in the seas

4   Coal is deposited on stagnant, vegetated delta tops

5   Large masses of hot magma heat the surrounding (or country) rocks, causing them to change into new metamorphic rocks

6   Hot water, rich in dissolved minerals, is driven away from cooling magma. It fills cavities in the country rock, within which large crystals may grow

7   Magma intrudes into the country rock, cooling to form igneous sills and dykes

8   Magma is formed from the melting crust and mantle

9   Volcanoes erupt ash and lava. Lava solidifies to form fine-grained igneous rocks

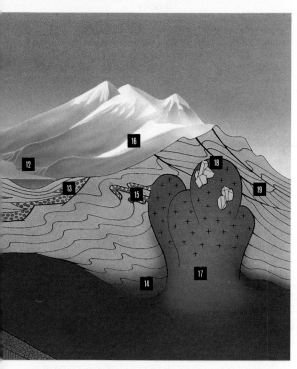

Sedimentary rocks	Minerals

10 Fragments of rock and mineral produced by the weathering of preexisting rocks accumulate in basins and become compacted into sedimentary rocks

11 Evaporation of water from lakes in hot, dry areas causes dissolved minerals to be deposited

12 Rivers transport and grade rock fragments

13 Some sedimentary rocks – such as breccia – contain very large pieces of parent rock

14 Intense pressure at depth in the crust alters the country rock, producing metamorphic rock

15 Hot water, rich in dissolved minerals, is driven away from cooling magma. It fills cavities and (hydrothermal) veins in the country rock, within which large crystals may grow

16 Glaciers transport rock fragments

17 Magma cools slowly at depth, forming coarse-grained igneous rock, typically granite

18 Igneous rocks known as pegmatites form in water-rich pockets of granite. Pegmatites typically bear well-formed and exceptionally large crystals of many different minerals

19 Rocks are compressed and crumple or break.

Rocks

Rocks are naturally-formed aggregates of minerals that make up all of the Earth's crust and the solid parts of the mantle below. Most are composed of several different types of mineral, though many of the rock-forming minerals are silicates (see p. 88). The physical characteristics of a rock are determined by the chemistry of its mineral constituents and by the processes that it endured during and since its formation. Crystallized in its structure, therefore, is a wealth of information about the conditions that once existed on the Earth's surface, and those found today at great depths within the planet. There are three types of rock – igneous, metamorphic and sedimentary – though as with all classifications, these divisions can be arbitrary.

Igneous rocks form as a magma (a hot, molten mass of mainly silica minerals) cools and solidifies. They can usually be identified because they are hard and have a homogenous texture – i.e. they tend to look the same in all directions, not changing in colour or grain size across a hand specimen. Constituent minerals are distributed randomly throughout the body of the rock.

Metamorphic rocks form by the alteration of existing rocks by heat or pressure. Although they are heated, these rocks never become molten, so as their constituent minerals recrystallize, they usually become aligned in the direction of least resistance – one that minimizes the effects of pressure on their structure. Metamorphic rocks are typically inhomogenous, containing parallel planes along which they split, or (often folded) bands of different minerals. All are relatively hard and brittle.

Sedimentary rocks are composed of mineral grains or rock fragments held together by fine debris or cementing minerals. They are deposited, layer by layer, on the surface of the Earth by the action of rivers, ocean currents, the work of organisms or the evaporation of water. They have a granular appearance, and since the cements that hold them together are relatively weak, they fragment easily.

The table below gives the main field characteristics of the three rock types. Grain structure is shown schematically, but may not be visible to the naked eye in fine-grained rocks

	Igneous Hard Brittle	Homogenous Cuts across country rock
	Metamorphic Hard Brittle	Bands of different minerals Minerals orientated Bands often folded
	Sedimentary Soft Brittle or ductile	Ripples Particles graded by size Cracks and fossils common

Igneous rocks

The raw material for all igneous rocks is magma – a hot, molten mass of minerals. Magmas form when the Earth's crust or upper mantle is heated and decompressed to the point at which it melts and begins to flow like a liquid. This requires enormous amounts of energy, which is available where the boundaries of the great plates that make up the crust collide or are pulled apart. When a magma subsequently cools, the minerals it contains crystallize, giving rise to igneous rock. Because the crystals form in a liquid, they are not forced to grow in any one direction, but are randomly aligned within the rock.

The characteristics of an igneous rock are determined by two important factors: the chemical composition of the parent magma; and how and where this magma cools.

Magma cooling

Magma that becomes trapped deep underground cools slowly; this means that large crystals have time to form, giving the resulting rock a coarse-grained appearance. Such magmas form gigantic pods of rock, which can have a volume of thousands of cubic kilometres. They eat through great patches of the surrounding (or country) rock, obliterating its structure.

Magma that intrudes to a higher level in the crust tends to flow along existing planes in the country rock, or along faults and joints – indeed anywhere that the crust is slightly weaker than average. Many shapes of intrusion form here, the most common of which are sills and dykes. Sills are sheets of magma which flow parallel to the bedding of the country rocks, while dykes cut across the grain. Rock formed from these magmas has an intermediate grain size.

When magma erupts on the surface of the Earth it is called lava. It flows from volcanoes, which are mountains built from successive lava and ash flows. This magma cools quickly and the crystals that grow are small, giving the resulting rock a fine-grained appearance.

Magma composition

The chemical composition of magmas is highly variable, though all have a high content of silicon and oxygen. Most minerals that crystallize from magmas are therefore, unsurprisingly, silicates (see p. 88). Some magmas are particularly rich in silicon; the rocks that they produce are composed of minerals that need a lot of silicon in their structure – typically quartz, feldspar and biotite. Silica-poor magmas produce rocks whose constituent minerals require less silicon – typically olivine, pyroxene and amphibole. These minerals contain much iron and magnesium, and are often referred to as the ferromagnesian minerals.

While it difficult to accurately identify the tiny crystals within an individual rock, silica-rich rocks are usually lighter in colour than silica-poor rocks. This makes the field classification of igneous rocks, taking into account colour and grain size, relatively easy (see table, p.10).

Distribution of igneous rocks

In general, silica-rich magmas form where the continental crust melts, while silica-poor magmas occur where the oceanic crust or upper mantle melt. The two types of magma have very different physical properties, which account for the distribution of rocks derived from them.

Silica-poor magmas are dense but have a low viscosity (i.e. they are very runny). Silica-rich magmas, on the other hand, are less dense but very viscous, having the consistency of tar. This is because the silica aggregates into long chains (polymers) which clog up the magma. Most silica-rich magma becomes trapped at depth within the crust because its high viscosity makes upward movement difficult. Coarse-grained rocks with high silica contents are therefore relatively common. Similarly, magmas that are very poor in silica are simply too heavy to reach the Earth's surface: consequently, there is no fine-grained equivalent of dunite (see table below).

Volcanoes that erupt silica-poor magma produce runny lava, which flows fast and for long distances over the ground, while volcanoes that erupt silica-rich magma produce sticky lava, which cannot flow far and solidifies close to the vent. Gas, which is abundant in all magmas, escapes easily from runny lavas, while in sticky magmas it is trapped. Pressure builds up in the trapped gas, causing large explosions that propel ash-filled clouds into the atmosphere. These clouds spread out over the surrounding country causing destruction and local climate change.

By far the most widespread lava is silica-poor basalt. It covers most of the ocean floor and huge areas of the continents, like the Deccan region of India and the Columbia River Plateau in North America.

A classification of igneous rocks according to grain size and silica content (colour). The schematic illustration on the right hand side shows the depth at which each rock type forms

Increasing silica content →

Grain Size	Dark		Light
	Basalt	Andesite	Rhyolite
			Obsidian
	Dolerite	Porphyry	
	Gabbro	Diorite	Syenite
	Dunite		Granite

Granite

One of the most widespread rocks in the continental crust. Coarse grained and light coloured, usually pink or greyish-white overall. Composed of quartz (glassy grey), feldspar (opaque pink or white) and a darker mineral, usually biotite. Usually homogenous in texture, but can show banding by composition or grain orientation. Often forms hills in moorland areas. Originates from deep seated, slow cooling of a silica-rich magma. It shows sharp intrusive, or blurred contacts with the surrounding rocks. Coarse granites are called pegmatites.

Obsidian

Dark green or black glass. Pronounced conchoidal fracture, with very sharp edges. Shatters on hitting and should not be hammered. Sometimes shows flow bands of lighter colour and bubbly texture, when it is locally called pitchstone. Formed by the rapid eruption and quenching of silica rich-magma.

Tuff

A light-coloured and generally fine-grained composite rock made from the explosive products of any volcanic eruption. Contains fragments of older rocks, and crystals and lava from the eruption which formed it. Can be layered, with typical sedimentary structures, like ripples and bedding.

11

Pumice

Fine-grained, light-coloured rock, usually white, grey or honey brown. Full of large bubble holes and highly porous. Has a low density and will float on water. An eruptive product of gas-rich, silica-rich magmas. Forms large rafts on water bodies when recently erupted. Weathers quickly to ashy sand as it is so porous and loosely cemented. Used as an abrasive and insulation material.

Andesite

Medium- to fine-grained, moderately light-coloured rock, usually grey to greenish-grey or brown. Homogenous texture, but often contains feldspar (white or pink) or biotite (black and platy) crystals which are much larger than the surrounding matrix. Forms broad lava flows from volcanoes which have moderately siliceous magma. Named after the Andes where it is abundant.

Rhyolite

Fine-grained, light-coloured (usually whitish) rock, often containing scattered larger crystals. Eruptive product of silica-rich magma, usually explosive in origin. It sometimes has a welded, fragmented appearance visible to the naked eye on close inspection. Covers large areas of New Zealand's North Island.

Gabbro

Coarse-grained, dark-coloured, usually grey or greenish. Sometimes magnetic and always unexpectedly heavy. Outcrops often show banding caused by variations in the concentration of the rock's component minerals, which are generally feldspar (whitish), ferromagnesian minerals (dark green or black) and metal oxides (black).

Porphyry

This is the general name for fine- to medium-grained rocks that have much larger crystals dispersed in their ground mass. Can be almost any colour – dark to light grey, brown, greenish, white. The rock name is given by the type of mineral present as large grains, e.g quartz porphyry. Moderately rich in silica, porphyrys form when a magma cools slowly at first to produce the large crystals, then more rapidly to produce the fine-grained ground mass.

Peridotite

Coarse-grained, homogenous rock, usually grey to black in colour, but may be green to pistachio green (when it contains only olivine and is known as dunite). Very dense, with interlocking crystals of ferromagnesian minerals and opaque metal oxides. Forms by slow cooling of silica-starved magmas deep in the crust. Weathers quickly on the surface to give a finer-grained, cracked and veined rock, which can be green, white, black, red or yellow in colour.

Syenite

A coarse-grained, light-coloured rock, most frequently a pink or grey colour. Syenite contains abundant feldspar, as well as biotite and an amphibole. Rarely contains quartz . It is a rare rock, usually occurring in small intrusions or at the edge of large granites.

Basalt

Fine-grained, dark-coloured, usually dark grey to black. Sometimes magnetic. Uniform texture, often with gas bubble holes. These can be filled with light-coloured minerals, often zeolites. Forms widespread lava flows from volcanoes that erupt silica-poor magma. Such flows typically become more gassy near the top and may have a cracked or ashy upper surface. Ropy flow patterns are sometimes visible.

Dolerite

Sometimes called diabase. Medium-grained dark grey rock with a speckled appearance and uniform texture. Can be magnetic. Forms high-level intrusions of silica-poor magma, usually dykes or sills. It contains feldspar, pyroxene and olivine, but these are difficult to identify in the field as they form very small grains. Dolerite weathers rapidly into rounded blocks of varying size.

Diorite

A coarse-grained rock, usually medium to dark grey in colour. It contains feldspar, biotite, amphibole and rarely pyroxene. Similar in composition to syenite, though it contains less silica. Most commonly found around the edges of granite intrusions. It weathers into more rounded shapes than either granite or syenite, and the dark minerals stand out as weathering proceeds.

Metamorphic rocks

Rocks are commonly regarded as being tough, immutable objects. Yet the minerals they contain are only stable under a certain set of temperature and pressure conditions. A significant change in those conditions will often cause a rock's constituents to recrystallize as an entirely new suite of minerals, producing a rock with very different characteristics to the parent type. This change is known as metamorphism. Rocks are metamorphosed whilst in the solid state. Because the rock never becomes molten, the minerals within it are subjected to directional pressure, and commonly become aligned in the direction of minimum stress. Metamorphic rocks therefore frequently have a banded appearance, in which parallel planes are visible.

The nature of the rock formed by metamorphism is determined by the composition of the original rock – which can be sedimentary, igneous or metamorphic in origin – and the degree of heat and pressure to which it has been subjected. For example, when clay is subjected to conditions of extreme heat but little pressure, spotted rock or hornfels are the metamorphic products: if it experiences great pressure but little heat, slate is formed. On the other hand, pure limestone can only be metamorphosed to one product (marble) regardless of the conditions it encounters. The presence or absence of fluids in rocks also influences the course of metamorphism. Metamorphic minerals are very diverse, and most are relatively rare because any given combination of heat, temperature and other conditions occurs only infrequently. After metamorphosis, the parent rock can be diagnosed by looking for mineral and structural remains.

Rocks are changed by heat and pressure while they heat up, and also as they cool down. The length of time spent doing either is another factor that influences the type of rock formed in metamorphosis.

Four broad categories of metamorphism are recognized; however, the processes that characterize each one are not mutually exclusive.

Thermal metamorphism

Rocks can be changed under conditions of high temperature and relatively low pressure. Such metamorphism is known as thermal, and typically occurs near large igneous intrusions, where magma raises the temperature of the surrounding country rock and causes a new set of "heat-tolerant" minerals to recrystallize. The metamorphic effect in these areas is also influenced by mineral-rich fluids, which are driven away from the cooling magma, and are important in determining the nature of the new minerals formed.

Dynamic metamorphism

Close to faults in the Earth's crust, and in folding rocks, metamorphism occurs mainly through the agent of pressure. Rocks, and even their constituent minerals, are broken, and recrystallization of "pressure-tolerant" minerals follows.

Regional metamorphism

The formation of many metamorphic rocks is related to neither igneous intrusions nor faults in the crust. The heat and pressure that change these rocks are properties of the Earth itself. Heat is generated in the crust through the decay of radioactive minerals, which are more common in the continental than in the oceanic crust. This heat is dispersed very slowly (because the overlying rock provides efficient insulation) and temperature therefore rises with depth, usually by around 15–30° C per km. Heat generated in the mantle also helps maintain the temperature gradient in the crust.

Pressure also increases with depth. Rocks buried 3 km down in the crust experience pressures 1,000 times greater than those on the surface; this is in addition to the directional pressures generated by the movement of crustal plates. As surface or near-surface rocks sink deeper into the crust, they become subject to these great temperatures and pressures, and their resulting recrystallization is known as regional metamorphism. Rocks formed by this type of metamorphism tend to contain a high proportion of lamellar minerals, such as mica.

Regional metamorphism is the most widespread and significant type. It is occurring today where mountain building is going on. This is generally where continents are in collision, for example where India is colliding with Asia to generate the Himalayas. Rocks being metamorphosed in these regions at present are many kilometres below the surface of the Earth and will only be exposed on the face of the planet after millions of years of erosion. Where these rocks are found on the surface, they represent an ancient phase of mountain building.

One belt of regionally-metamorphosed rocks runs from northern Scandinavia, through Scotland and south-east Canada, and down the chain of the Appalachians on the eastern seaboard of Northern America. Along this chain, the presence of regionally-metamorphosed rocks indicates that high mountains once existed. Dating of the associated granites shows that these reached their highest point about 350 million years ago. At this time, well before the opening of the Atlantic, mountains extended in a single continuous chain for over 5,000km, from Spitsbergen to Florida.

Impact metamorphism

Very occasionally, metamorphism is caused by the high-speed impact of a meteorite with the Earth's surface, which generates local conditions of high temperature and pressure. Because this metamorphism occurs on the surface, its products are rapidly eroded by natural processes, so are observed only when the collision occurred fairly recently.

Gneiss

Coarse-grained, crystalline, banded rock. Quartz and feldspar-rich bands alternate with darker bands of variable mineralogy. Bands often show foliation. Large, well-shaped crystals of metamorphic minerals, such as garnet and kyanite are often present. Formed by high-grade regional metamorphism.

Hornfels

Granular texture, medium- to coarse-grained. Colour varies – can be black, grey, green, brown, pink or purple. Generally has a battered appearance. Formed by high-grade contact metamorphism of most fine- and medium-grained rocks. The minerals present in hornfels have grown during metamorphism and cut across earlier strucures, such as bedding planes. Found adjacent to large igneous intrusions.

Phyllite

Medium- to fine-grained rock. Usually light grey, sometimes greenish in colour. It is foliated, splitting along wavy partings, the surfaces of which have a metallic lustre caused by mica plates which have grown along them. Produced by slightly higher-grade regional metamorphism than slate, but of the same original rock type. Phyllite is intermediate between slate and schist.

17

Slate

Fine-grained rock, grey, green, black, deep red or purple in colour. Brittle, and splits easily along planes of cleavage that result from the alignment under pressure of tiny, flat minerals. These minerals are usually micas – either muscovite or biotite. They give cleavage surfaces a permanently-wet look.

Cleavage often cuts across bedding, which is still visible in many slates. Formed by the dynamic or low-grade regional metamorphism of fine-grained sediments. Found in ancient and modern mountain belts. The strength and closely-spaced cleavage of slate have led to its widespread use as a roofing material.

Schist

Generally grey or silver in colour, less frequently pink or golden. A coarse-grained rock, which contains much mica. This platy mineral grows under directional pressure in schist, giving the rock a highly foliated appearance, like the leaves of a book. The sheets of mica overlap, giving the rock a shiny look. Coarse crystals of rarer minerals also occur in schist and displace the bands of mica. Garnets of various types and kyanite grow in these situations.

Schist is formed from the medium-grade regional metamorphism of fine-grained, clay-rich sediment.

Granulite

Coarse-grained, homogenous, crystalline rock with abundant feldspar, quartz and garnet. Pale to dark grey in colour. Forms from high-grade regional metamorphism which occurs in the deeper parts of the Earth's crust. Granulite is so highly metamorphosed that it almost becomes molten during its formation. Slightly more heat and pressure would produce granite. It is often found in veins, and forms intrusive contacts with other rocks.

Quartzite

Granular, pale-coloured rock, most frequently pink or white. It is made up almost entirely of quartz. If traces of other minerals are present, it can appear grey to black. Very hard, often ringing dully if hammered. Forms by any type of metamorphism of quartz-rich sediments. The constituent quartz grains are merely sutured together by metamorphic pressures and temperatures, rather than being transformed into other minerals.

Marble

Grain size fine to sugar-like; colour variable. Pure marble, which is composed entirely of calcite, is white, but slight impurities can give streaks or patches of red, yellow, green, grey, or any combination of these. Forms as a result of contact, regional or dynamic metamorphism of largely pure limestones. Impure or contaminated limestones give rise to assemblages of rare minerals – the rocks known as skarns. Widely used in both polished and unpolished forms as a building and ornamental material.

Sedimentary rocks

Of the three major rock types, sedimentary rocks are the most common on the Earth's surface. They are unique in that they are laid down on the face of the planet, rather than deep within it; their examination can therefore yield important information about the conditions on the surface at the time of their formation. Two broad categories of sedimentary rocks are recognized – the clastic sediments and the biological or chemical sediments.

Clastic sediments

These rocks form by the breakdown of existing rocks of any type into fragments (clasts), which are then carried some distance by natural processes, deposited, and finally compacted or cemented into a new rock type. Clasts are broken from their parent rock by a variety of processes. The freezing and thawing of water in cracks, the grinding action of glaciers, and the pounding of waves can all fragment a rock into clasts of various sizes. Clasts are often angular when they are first formed. These rock fragments are then transported, often by fast flowing rivers, away from their region of formation. Transport by water abrades the clasts, making them more rounded, and reduces their size. Other transport processes are also important; for example, clasts can be trapped in slow-moving glaciers. Transport by ice maintains the angularity of the particles.

The way in which clasts are transported partly determines the type of sedimentary rock formed: angular clasts form rocks containing angular fragments, for example. More significantly, transport grades the clasts by size or by weight. Pebbles are too heavy to be carried by slow-moving rivers and are typically deposited on river beds, while finer clasts are often deposited in lakes. Many river-borne fragments are carried all the way to the sea; again they are graded, with different sized clasts deposited according to distance from the coast.

Once deposited, the loose sediment is physically or chemically bound into rock. It is either compacted by the great weight of sediment above it, or is cemented together by a chemical "glue" usually made of silica or calcite.

Since clasts are derived from almost all rock types, one would expect sedimentary rocks to be composed of a large array of minerals. However, many minerals – including feldspar, biotite and all of the ferromagnesian minerals – break down rapidly when exposed to conditions on the Earth's surface. Conversely, quartz is stable under such conditions. It is not surprising, therefore, that sediments which have been exposed to surface processes for a long time tend to be richer in quartz than those produced recently from a primary source. Rocks that contain fragments of feldspar and biotite are particularly affected by water. They take up large quantities into their structure and break down to form clays.

When examining clastic sediments in the field, size and angularity of clasts are the most reliable diagnostic features.

Chemical and biological sediments

These rocks form as a result of biological and chemical processes occurring on the surface of the Earth. Limestone is the most common rock made in this way. It is composed almost entirely of $CaCO_3$, usually in the form of the mineral calcite, and contains varying amounts of iron and magnesium impurities. Calcite is present in seawater. Cold seawater can hold much more dissolved calcite than warm seawater, so in areas where the sea is warm and shallow, calcite is forced to precipitate on the sea floor. It is also extracted from seawater by living organisms, which use it to build their skeletons. On death, these skeletons fall to the sea floor and become consolidated into limestones.

Similar processes occur in landlocked lakes in dry areas. If water evaporates from the lake more quickly than it can be replaced, the minerals dissolved in the water are precipitated and form sediments. Rocks formed in this way are called evaporites. They frequently contain minerals such as gypsum and halite. All evaporite minerals are soluble in water.

Evaporites are forming today in shallow water and shoreline environments between 17° and 35° of latitude. In the geological record there are massive thicknesses of evaporites which appear to have no modern analogue. The most spectacular of these are around the Mediterranean basin, where thicknesses locally exceed 2 km. The evaporation of 1,000 m of sea water produces 14 m of evaporite: since the Mediterranean is a maximum of 5 km deep, it must have completely evaporated 30 times, or been constantly resupplied by water from the Atlantic in order to have deposited the observed thickness of salts.

Fossil fuels, broadly coal, oil and gas, are derived from the organic remains of animals and plants. By volume they make up a small part of the sedimentary record, but they are of huge economic significance. Coal and its associated rocks form mainly from woody plants which lived on land. Oil and gas form from the remains of microscopic marine plants and animals (plankton). All of these rock types need time and fairly deep burial to develop. The water and trace elements of the organic remains are driven off, leaving mainly carbon and oxygen. The final product of coal formation is thin beds of solid rock, interspersed between the organic sediments. The final product of oil formation is still liquid, and needs to be trapped between two impermeable rock layers.

The rock cycle

The elements that make up rock-forming minerals are never lost, but are recycled in the Earth's crust and upper mantle. Igneous rocks can be eroded to form sediments, or metamorphosed by heat and pressure. Sediments can also be metamorphosed, or completely melted to form magma. This can happen to a metamorphic rock, or it can be eroded on the surface producing a sediment.

21

A

B

Conglomerate

Coarse-grained rock made up of rounded fragments, 2 mm or more in length, set in a finer matrix. Fragments can be of one or more rock type; colour is therefore variable and patchy. Grading and imbrication, where the fragments are stacked all pointing in the same direction, are common. Fossils are rare. The percentage of clasts relative to matrix is highly variable and reflects the origin of deposition. Contrast the slump deposit (A) with the specimen of rock laid down in water (B).

Breccia

Coarse-grained rock made up of angular fragments, more than 2 mm long, set in a finer matrix. Fragments can be of one or, less commonly, several rock types. Fossils are very rare. Grading from coarse to fine fragments can be present but the rock is often massive. In extreme cases, fragments can exceed 100 m in length. Forms by rapid erosion and deposition, such as that brought about by landslides and cave-ins.

Evaporite

Usually light coloured, white, yellow or pink. Most can be scratched with a fingernail. These rocks are composed of a range of minerals, including gypsum and halite that are deposited from water as it evaporates. They form wherever the rate of evaporation exceeds rainfall. Usually soluble in water, they have a short residence time on the surface as they are quickly eroded by rain.

Sandstone

(Orthoquartzite). Grains 0.02 to 2 mm in diameter, dominated by quartz. Normally white or yellow, can be red, green, brown, grey. Usually bedded, often-cross bedded, rippled or graded. Fossils occur. Formed by prolonged transport of grains so that they become sorted and rounded.

Sandstone

(Arkose). Grains 0.02 to 2 mm in diameter, made up of fragments of feldspar (white or pink and opaque) and quartz (greyish or yellowish and glassy). Grey, brown, pink or reddish in overall colour. Usually bedded, often cross-bedded, rippled or graded. Fossils occur. Formed by the erosion of granites, gneisses or schists, followed by transport over a relatively short distance.

Sandstone

(Greywacke). Grains 0.02 to 2mm in diameter, made up of fragments of quartz and rock fragments, with minor feldspar. Generally dark in colour – grey, greenish-grey or brown. Usually bedded, often cross- bedded, rippled or graded. Fossils occur. Formed in the early stages of mountain building, when uplift leads to rapid erosion and transport. Often deposited in deep water.

Clay

Sticky, unconsolidated, fine-grained sediment. Clasts less than 0.004 mm in diameter. Colour variable, may be white, yellow, red, green, purple, blue, grey or black. Fossils common. Deposited in still water. Also formed by weathering of granites. Used extensively for pottery, since clay minerals bake hard when subjected to high temperatures.

Lignite

Soft, black, brown or yellowish coal. Woody structure of the original plants is still visible. Relatively low carbon content (about 30%). Lignite is younger than most coals, but older than peat. It has experienced burial to moderate depths, and has been heated slightly. Burns smokily and produces large quantities of ash; nevertheless, it is used as a fuel in many countries, especially where true coal is rare. It is burned in power stations more often than in domestic fires.

Siltstone

Fine-grained rock. Clasts are 0.004 to 0.02 mm in diameter. Grey, brown, green, or red in colour. Usually finely bedded, sometimes rippled. Fossils common. A finer-grained version of sandstone, composed of a similar suite of minerals. Siltstone can be deposited by wind or water.

Limestone
Usually light in colour, white or grey, but can be black if impurities are present. Grain typically fine, but ranges from the microscopic to the size of a coral reef, which technically corresponds to one "grain". Made up of calcite or another carbonate and can therefore be identified by dropping dilute hydrochloric acid on to its surface – the rock releases carbon dioxide, fizzing vigorously. Fossils very common.

Flint and chert
Usually grey, black, or brown in colour. Found as fine-grained or glassy nodules or bands made of quartz. Usually brown or black in colour. Hard, breaking with a conchoidal fracture to give sharp edges; should not be hammered. Formed from the microscopic skeletons of siliceous marine plants and the skeletal remains of some sponges. Used by stone age people to produce bladed tools.

Chalk
Common type of limestone; fine grained, soft and white. Often lacks bedding or other sedimentary stuctures. Composed of the microscopic bodies of marine plants called coccolithophores, which have calcite skeletons. Other fossils sometimes present. Often contains rows of siliceous nodules; these can follow or cut bedding.

Shale

Fissile, fine-grained sediment. Clasts less than 0.004 mm in diameter. Usually dark grey in colour but can also be green, red, purple or light grey. Grains too small to see with the naked eye are rich in clay minerals. Deposited in still water or where other sediment is scarce. Compressed by burial, which gives rise to fissility. Fossils are often present (note the shell fragments in the specimen shown), and the fine grain of the rock means that great detail can be preserved in fossilized material.

Peat

Present only as surface deposits and usually waterlogged. Most common in northern Europe, where it is accompanied by a distinctive suite of plants that can survive the high acidity produced as organic matter decays. Peat is a recent deposit, which alters over time into lignite, coal or anthracite. It is brown, reddish or black in colour, and made up of fibrous plant debris. Whole branches and tree-stumps are often preserved in peat, along with pollen and soft animal tissues (sometimes even the remains of early people).

Coal

Black in colour, with an even texture and a lustre that varies from shiny to dull. The shiny varieties are called vitrain, and are most prized by miners. Generally soft, but brittle when hit. Occurs in beds between shales, sandstones and limestones. Beds range from 1 mm to 4 m in thickness. Coal is a highly compressed and much older form of peat from which impurities and water have been driven off by burial. Has a high carbon content (up to 60%) so burns cleanly, producing little ash or smoke.

Anthracite

Hard, glossy, black coal with a conchoidal fracture. Produced by low-grade metamorphism of coal, which occurs during deep burial beneath a thick pile of sediments. It is a good fuel, with a high carbon content (up to 95%), and burns producing very little ash.

Minerals

A mineral is a naturally-formed, solid, crystalline substance. It has a specific chemical composition, and its atoms are arranged in a regular and ordered framework – a crystal. Pure halite (NaCl), for example, always contains sodium and chlorine atoms in the same proportions; and if allowed to crystallize freely, it always forms cubic crystals.

The vast majority of minerals in the Earth's crust are constituents of rocks. Their crystals are tiny and have been deformed by the need to squeeze into small spaces, or have been ground down during the formation of sedimentary rock. The large well-shaped crystals sought by collectors grow in more favourable environments, often close to developing igneous rocks. These rocks form when molten magma cools and solidifies. During the cooling, superheated water, rich in dissolved mineral-forming elements, is driven away from the magma. It fills cracks and crevices in the surrounding rock, and crystals grow slowly as the water cools. This process takes anything up to half a million years, and can be disrupted by small changes in temperature or pressure.

A mineral derives its physical properties from its chemical composition and its structure. For instance, the mineral thorianite contains uranium, and is radioactive for that reason alone: its radioactivity is not dependent on the arrangement of uranium atoms within the mineral. Conversely, carbon exists as two mineral types – graphite and diamond. Both are made of the same element, but in different arrangements: graphite is one of the softest minerals known, diamond the hardest.

The different properties of minerals include obvious things like colour, hardness and weight (or specific gravity), and perhaps less obvious characteristics such as streak, lustre and form. An understanding of these properties is crucial to the accurate identification of specimens.

Colour

In some minerals, colour is a constant and distinctive feature – a good aid to identification. Malachite, for example, is always green, and orpiment is always yellow. In these cases the colour is produced by a necessary part of the mineral's chemistry or structure. More often, a mineral's colour is variable and is produced by the presence of impurities or defects in the way the crystal has grown. Quartz is an ideal example of this. Pure, perfectly-formed quartz is transparent and colourless. Tiny amounts of iron in its structure will turn it yellow (citrine), and equally small amounts of manganese will turn it pink. In this case colour is not a useful diagnostic property. Most minerals fall between these two extremes. They can exhibit a range of colours but within certain useful limits. For example, sphalerite can be yellow, orange, red, brown or black but it is never blue or purple. When looking at the colour of a mineral it is important always to examine fresh surfaces.

Streak

This is the colour of a mineral when it is powdered, or the colour of the streak it leaves behind when rubbed on an unglazed porcelain surface. If the colour of the mineral is determined by an essential chemical component, as in the case of malachite, then streak colour will be the same as body colour, but rather lighter. It is useful to check the streak of very dark minerals: they may look black but have a dark, coloured streak. If a mineral's colour is caused by impurities or imperfections in the crystal structure, then the streak is usually white. Minerals that have a hardness greater than about 6.5 on Mohs' scale (see *Hardness and tenacity*) leave no streak on a porcelain tile, and cannot be tested in this way.

Lustre

Minerals can have a variety of different surface textures and can reflect light to varying degrees. These surface properties are together called lustre. The terms used to describe lustre are usually self explanatory – metallic, glassy, resinous, silky, greasy and earthy. Many names can be applied, but the choice is a subjective one. A lustre described as greasy by one person may look glassy to another.

Hardness and tenacity

Some minerals are clearly hard and resistant to scratching and abrasion. Most gemstones are hard enough to keep a high polish through day-to-day wear and tear. At the other end of the scale, gypsum and graphite are soft enough to be scratched with a fingernail. Measuring the hardness of minerals is done on a relative scale devised by a german mineralogist named Mohs. Mohs' scale lists ten minerals in order of increasing hardness. Other minerals of unknown hardness can then be ranked relative to these known constants. A harder mineral will always scratch a softer one.

Mohs' scale of minerals is:

1	Talc	6	Orthoclase feldspar
2	Gypsum	7	Quartz
3	Calcite	8	Topaz
4	Fluorite	9	Corundum
5	Apatite	10	Diamond

Sets of these reference minerals can be bought, but a rougher guide can be obtained from objects readily available in most homes. A fingernail, for instance, has a hardness between 2 and 2.5 (unless it has been bitten!). A more accessible scale for comparison of hardness is used in the identification tables of this book (see *Using the tables*, p.33).

Minerals also have a characteristic tenacity. This is a measure of behaviour under stress. Brittle minerals fracture if cut or hit. Sectile minerals can be cut with a knife. Malleable minerals can be hammered into thin sheets.

Crystal systems

Crystals fall into one of seven distinct classes of symmetry, known as crystal systems. Three-dimensional symmetry is best explained by first considering a two-dimensional square rotated through 360° around its centre. The square shape repeats itself four times in each complete rotation and is said to have a four-fold axis of symmetry. A hexagon repeats itself six times, a triangle three times etc. Similar axes can be found in three-dimensional shapes. In the diagrams below, arrows show the location of axes of symmetry, and the small two-dimensional shapes indicate the number of times the crystal repeats itself when rotated around that axis.

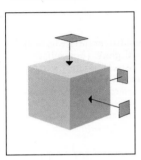

Cubic system

Three four-fold axes of symmetry at right angles to one another. See galena, garnet group, halite.

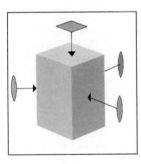

Tetragonal system

One four-fold axis of symmetry and several two-fold axes at right angles to it. See chalcopyrite.

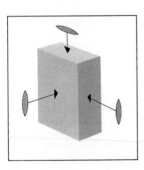

Orthorhombic system

Three two-fold axes of symmetry at right angles to one another. See barite, andalusite.

Minerals

Monoclinic system

One two-fold axis of symmetry. See gypsum, titanite, biotite.

Triclinic system

No symmetry axes at all. See axinite, plagioclase feldspars.

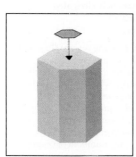

Hexagonal system

One six-fold axis of symmetry. See beryl, apatite.

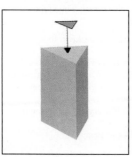

Trigonal system

One three-fold axis of symmetry. See quartz, calcite, corundum.

31

Specific gravity

The weight of a mineral relative to the weight of water it displaces is known as its specific gravity. A mineral with a specific gravity of 7 weighs seven times as much as its own volume of water. An accurate measure of specific gravity is obtained in the following way. The mineral is weighed in air, and again when suspended in water. The difference between these values gives the weight of an equal volume of water. The specific gravity is then calculated:

> *Specific gravity = weight of mineral in air/weight of an equal volume of water*

With some experience, specific gravity can be estimated by just handling the specimen. Some minerals feel surprisingly heavy or unexpectedly light for their size.

Habit and form

A mineral may be found as a single large crystal, or as groups of crystals growing together. It could resmble a massive lump or a network of radiating fibres. The appearance of a mineral specimen is known as its form.

Single, well-developed crystals grow only in ideal conditions, and then only in some minerals. Where such crystals are found, shape is a useful diagnostic feature. The most common crystal shapes are:

> Prismatic: elongated, rather pencil-like
> Needle-like or acicular: extremely elongated
> Bladed: resembling a knife blade
> Tabular: like pieces of paper

One mineral may be capable of forming several shapes of crystal. Pyrite crystals, for example, may be cubic or octohedral. However, crystals of the same mineral will share certain features of symmetry, which can be used to help identify them (see *Crystal systems,* p. 30).

Crystals are more often found in groups than singly. Sometimes pairs or sets of crystals grow together, interlocking with one another: such arrangements are known as twins. Alternatively, large numbers of separate and unrelated crystals of the same mineral occur together in aggregates. The appearance of these aggregates is often very different from that of a single crystal. The most common forms of aggregate are:

> Dendritic or branching: rather tree-like in form
> Reniform: kidney shaped
> Botryoidal: shaped like a bunch of grapes
> Massive: interlocking grains with a poor crystal shape
> Fibrous: thread-like fibres, often matted together or laid parallel
> Radiating : fibres or needle-like crystals growing out from a centre
> Stalactitic: thin columns like icicles

How to identify minerals

To date, about 2,500 minerals have been classified, and about fifty are added to this list annually. This book describes only a fraction of that number. It includes the most commonly-found minerals, which are described in greater length than the others, and a selection from the rest. The "common" minerals will not always be the ones you find. In any one area, an unusual mineral may predominate, or by diligence or luck one of the rarer types may be found.

On pages 44-117, a photograph of each mineral is accompanied by a brief description. The text in italics gives the mineral's chemical formula, its hardness on Mohs' scale (*H*), its specific gravity (*S.G.*), the crystal system to which it belongs, and the environments in which it typically forms. The remaining text details the mineral's colour, streak, lustre, tenacity, habit, form and any other diagnostic features. Within the book, minerals are arranged by chemical composition: so, for example, the carbonates appear on pp. 69-73. The general characteristics of each major chemical subdivision are described in a brief introduction. Some minerals, particularly among the silicates, are classified into groups or series, the members of which are chemically similar.

Using the tables

The tables on pages 34-43 have been designed to speed up mineral identification. Minerals are grouped together by colour. Those with more than one colour variety, are listed in each applicable section. So zircon, for example, which can be brown, green, orange, red, yellow or white, appears in each of these sections of the table. Common minerals have an asterisk after their names in the left hand column. Within each colour section, minerals are ranked by increasing hardness. Minerals are graded A-E as follows:

A: can be scratched by a fingernail (Mohs' equivalent about 2.5)
B: can be scratched by a copper coin (Mohs' equivalent 3)
C: can be scratched by window glass (Mohs' equivalent 5.5)
D: can be scratched by hardened steel (Mohs' equivalent 6.5)
E: Too hard to scratch with any common object

Knowing the colour and hardness of your mineral, and after checking its streak, you should be left with just a few "possibles". The right hand column lists other distinctive features that may be useful in identification. When you think you have identified your mineral, look up the full description and photograph: the page number is given on the right hand side of the table. Your specimen may well be a different colour or be in a different habit to the one shown. Do not be put off if your specimen looks different to the photograph; if it agrees with the description then your mineral is probably correctly identified. Good hunting!

MINERAL	HARDNESS/STREAK		OTHER FEATURES/PAGE	

BLACK

MINERAL		HARDNESS/STREAK	OTHER FEATURES	PAGE
Graphite	A	Grey-black	Greasy feel	46
Biotite *	B	White	Flexible micaceous cleavage	114
Bournonite	B	Grey-black	Cog wheel-twinned crystals	56
Chalcocite	B	Grey	Bright metallic	49
Enargite	B	Black	Metallic	49
Jamesonite	B	Grey-black	Iridescent metallic	54
Pyrargyrite	B	Red	Dull metallic	49
Silver	B	Shining grey	Heavy, malleable	45
Calcite *	C	White	Fizzes in dilute HCl	70
Cerussite	C	White		73
Descloizite	C	Yellow, orange, brownish		79
Goethite	C	Brownish-yellow		65
Kyanite	C	White	Hardness E along one axis	88
Manganite	C	Reddish-brown or black	Metallic	66
Siderite *	C	White		71
Sphalerite *	C	Pale-brown		52
Tetrahedrites	C	Brown-black		55
Titanite	C	White	Wedge-shaped crystals	89
Wavellite	C	White		78
Wolframite *	C	Reddish-brown to black	Dull metallic	75
Actinolite	D	White	Cleavage at 56° and 124°	99
Aegerine	D	Pale yellow-grey	Cleavage at 87° and 93°	101
Anatase	D	White	Slightly metallic	62
Augite	D	Greyish-white	Cleavage at 87° and 93°	101
Brookite	D	White, grey or yellow	Dull metallic	63
Cassiterite *	D	Dirty white		64
Chromite	D	Brown		65
Columbites – tantalites	D	Black or dark red	Crystals often heart-shaped	66
Diopside	D	Greyish-white	Cleavage at 87° and 93°	101
Glaucophane	D	Grey-blue	Cleavage at 56° and 124°	98
Hornblende	D	White	Cleavage at 56° and 124°	98
Hypersthene	D	Greyish-white	Cleavage at 87° and 93°	100
Ilmenite	D	Black	Metallic when fresh	66
Magnetite *	D	Black	Strongly magnetic	63
Opal	D	White	Iridescent lustre	106
Plagioclase *	D	White	Small bladed crystals	108
Psilomelane	D	Shining black		65
Pyrolusite	D	Black or blue-black		62
Riebeckite	D	White	Cleavage at 56° and 124°	98
Specular hematite *	D	Red	Bright metallic	61
Uraninite	D	Black, grey, olive green	Radioactive	67
Diamond	E	None	Adamantine lustre	44
Epidote	E	Grey-white	Long, slender striated prisms	93
Garnet *	E	White	Noticeably equant grains	90
Quartz *	E	White	Pyramidal crystals	102
Spinel	E	Colourless	Crystals small, octahedral	67
Tourmaline *	E	Too hard to streak	Long triangular crystals	95

BLUE

MINERAL		HARDNESS/STREAK	OTHER FEATURES	PAGE
Covellite	A	Grey-black	Dull metallic	53
Molybdenite	A	Blue-grey	Metallic, greasy feel	52
Sylvite	A	White	Soluble in water; bitter	60
Bornite	B	Grey-black	Metallic, iridescent	49
Brucite	B	White		67
Chalcanthite	B	White	Soluble in water	83
Chrysocolla	B	White to pale turquoise		117
Halite *	B	White	Soluble in water; salty	58
Langite	B	White		86

MINERAL	HARDNESS/STREAK		OTHER FEATURES/PAGE	
Linarite	B	Blue		85
Apatite	C	White		76
Aragonite *	C	White	Fizzes in dilute HCl	71
Azurite	C	Blue		72
Calcite *	C	White	Fizzes in dilute HCl	70
Celestite	C	White	Heavenly blue colour	85
Cerussite	C	White		73
Fluorite *	C	White		59
Hemimorphite	C	White		94
Kyanite	C	White	Hardness E along one axis	88
Lazurite	C	Blue		110
Smithsonite	C	White		72
Tetrahedrites	C	Brown-black		55
Anatase	D	White	Slightly metallic	62
Glaucophane	D	Grey-blue	Cleavage at 56° and 124°	98
Nepheline	D	White		110
Opal	D	White	Iridescent lustre	106
Plagioclase *	D	White	Small bladed crystals	108
Riebeckite	D	White	Cleavage at 56° and 124°	98
Rutile	D	Brown to yellow	Metallic; needle-like	68
Sodalite	D	White		110
Turquoise	D	White to pale green	Porcelain colour	80
Zoisite	D	White		93
Beryl	E	Too hard to streak	Six-sided crystals	96
Corundum	E	Colourless		68
Cristobalite	E	White	Octagonal crystals	106
Quartz *	E	White	Pyramidal crystals	102
Sillimanite	E	White		89
Spinel	E	Colourless	Crystals small, octahedral	67
Topaz	E	White		92
Vesuvianite	E	White	Prismatic crystals	94

BROWN				
Molybdenite	A	Blue-grey	Metallic; greasy feel	52
Stibnite *	A	Grey	Bright metallic	57
Gypsum *	A	White		84
Pyrophillite	A	White		117
Stolzite	A	Colourless		75
Biotite *	B	White	Flexible micaceous cleavage	114
Brucite	B	White		67
Chlorite	B	White	Micaceous cleavage	113
Cinnabar	B	Red		53
Copper	B	Shining pale red	Heavy, malleable, metallic	46
Hydrozincite	B	White		72
Jarosite	B	Yellow		86
Muscovite *	B	White	Flexible micaceous cleavage	114
Phlogopite	B	White	Flexible micaceous cleavage	115
Thenhardite	B	White	Soluble in water; salty	86
Vanadinite	B	White to pale yellow		80
Wulfenite	B	White		74
Apatite	C	White		76
Aragonite *	C	White	Fizzes in dilute HCl	71
Calcite *	C	White	Fizzes in dilute HCl	70
Descloizite	C	Yellow, orange, brownish		79
Goethite	C	Brownish-yellow		65
Hemimorphite	C	White		94
Magnesite	C	White		73
Mimetite	C	White		77
Monazite	C	White	Radioactive	80

MINERAL	HARDNESS/STREAK		OTHER FEATURES/PAGE	
Mottramite	C	Greenish-brown		79
Niccolite	C	Brown	Metallic	57
Olivenite	C	Yellow		79
Pyromorphite	C	White		77
Pyrrhotite	C	Grey-black	Metallic, often iridescent	57
Scheelite	C	White		75
Siderite *	C	White		71
Smithsonite	C	White		72
Sphalerite *	C	Pale brown		52
Stilbite	C	White	Cruciform penetration twins	112
Tetrahedrites	C	Brown-black		55
Titanite	C	White	Wedge-shaped crystals	89
Wavellite	C	White		78
Wolframite *	C	Reddish-brown to black	Dull metallic	75
Aegerine	D	Pale yellow-grey	Cleavage at 87° and 93°	101
Augite	D	Greyish-white	Cleavage at 87° and 93°	101
Anatase	D	White	Slightly metallic	62
Brookite	D	White, grey or yellow	Dull metallic	63
Cassiterite *	D	Dirty white		64
Columbites – tantalites	D	Black or dark red	Crystals often heart-shaped	66
Diopside	D	Greyish-white	Cleavage at 87° and 93°	101
Jadeite	D	White	Cleavage at 87° and 93°	101
Nephrite	D	White	Cleavage at 56° and 124°	99
Opal	D	White	Iridescent lustre	106
Potash feldspars *	D	White	Twinning common	107
Rhodonite	D	White	Often black-veined	97
Rutile	D	Brown to yellow	Metallic; needle-like	68
Uraninite	D	Black, grey, olive green	Radioactive	67
Zoisite	D	White		93
Axinite	E	White	Wedge-shaped crystal	95
Chrysoberyl	E	Colourless	Crystals often heart-shaped	62
Cordierite	E	Too hard to streak		96
Corundum	E	Colourless		68
Cristobalite	E	White	Octagonal crystals	106
Diamond	E	None	Adamantine lustre	44
Epidote	E	Grey-white	Long, slender striated prisms	93
Garnet *	E	White	Noticeably equant grains	90
Olivine *	E	White		89
Quartz *	E	White	Pyramidal crystals	102
Spinel	E	Colourless	Crystals small, octahedral	67
Staurolite	E	White	Cruciform twins occur	92
Tourmaline *	E	Too hard to streak	Long triangular crystals	95
Vesuvianite	E	White	Prismatic crystals	94
Zircon	E	White		92

GREEN				
Annabergite	A	Green		78
Carnotite	A	Yellow	Radioactive	79
Pyrophillite	A	White		117
Stolzite	A	Colourless		75
Talc	A	White	Greasy lustre	117
Autunite	B	Yellow	Radioactive	77
Biotite *	B	White	Flexible micaceous cleavage	114
Brucite	B	White		67
Chalcanthite	B	White	Soluble in water	83
Chlorite	B	White	Micaceous cleavage	113
Chrysocolla	B	White to pale turquoise		117
Glauconite	B	White	Greensand	114
Langite	B	White		86

MINERAL	HARDNESS/STREAK		OTHER FEATURES/PAGE	
Muscovite *	B	White	Flexible micaceous cleavage	114
Torbernite	B	Green	Radioactive	77
Adamite	C	White		81
Analcime	C	White	Usually in crystal form	112
Apatite	C	White		76
Apophyllite	C	White	Near cubic crystals	116
Aragonite *	C	White	Fizzes in dilute HCl	71
Cerussite	C	White		73
Dioptase	C	Pale greenish-blue		96
Fluorite *	C	White		59
Hemimorphite	C	White		94
Kyanite	C	White	Hardness E along one axis	88
Malachite *	C	Green		69
Mottramite	C	Greenish brown		79
Natrolite	C	White	Usually in crystal form	111
Olivenite	C	Yellow		79
Pyromorphite	C	White		77
Scheelite	C	White		75
Siderite *	C	White		71
Smithsonite	C	White		72
Sphalerite *	C	Pale brown		52
Strontianite	C	White	Fizzes in dilute HCl	73
Titanite	C	White	Wedge-shaped crystals	89
Variscite	C	White		78
Wavellite	C	White		78
Actinolite	D	White	Cleavage at 56° and 124°	99
Aegerine	D	Pale yellow-grey	Cleavage at 87° and 93°	101
Anatase	D	White	Slightly metallic	62
Augite	D	Greyish-white	Cleavage at 87° and 93°	101
Cassiterite *	D	Dirty white		64
Diopside	D	Greyish-white	Cleavage at 87° and 93°	101
Hornblende	D	White	Cleavage at 56° and 124°	98
Jadeite	D	White	Cleavage at 87° and 93°	101
Nepheline	D	White		110
Nephrite	D	White	Cleavage at 56° and 124°	99
Opal	D	White	Iridescent lustre	106
Plagioclase *	D	White	Small bladed crystals	108
Potash feldspars *	D	White	Twinning common	107
Prehnite	D	White	Barrel-like crystals	116
Rutile	D	Brown to yellow	Metallic; needle-like	68
Sodalite	D	White		110
Spodumene	D	White	Cleavage at 87° and 93°	101
Turquoise	D	White to pale green	Porcelain colour	80
Beryl	E	Too hard to streak	Six-sided crystals	96
Chrysoberyl	E	Colourless	Crystals often heart-shaped	62
Corundum	E	Colourless		68
Epidote	E	Grey-white	Long, slender striated prisms	93
Garnet *	E	White	Noticeably equant grains	90
Olivine *	E	White		89
Quartz *	E	White	Pyramidal crystals	102
Spinel	E	Colourless	Crystals small, octahedral	67
Topaz	E	White		92
Tourmaline *	E	Too hard to streak	Long triangular crystals	95
Vesuvianite	E	White	Prismatic crystals	94
Zircon	E	White		92

GREY				
Graphite	A	Grey-black	Greasy feel	46
Gypsum *	A	White		84

MINERAL	HARDNESS/STREAK	OTHER FEATURES/PAGE	
Molybdenite	A Blue-grey	Metallic; greasy feel	52
Stibnite	A Grey	Bright metallic	57
Sylvite	A White	Soluble in water; bitter	60
Anglesite	B Grey-white		83
Bismuth	B Silver-white	Metallic; tarnishes	46
Bismuthinite	B Grey	Metallic	51
Boulangerite	B Brown	Dull metallic	55
Bournonite	B Grey-black	Cog wheel-twinned crystals	56
Brucite	B White		67
Chalcocite	B Grey	Bright metallic	49
Chlorargyrite	B White	Soluble in water	58
Galena *	B Grey	Bright metallic when fresh	50
Halite *	B White	Soluble in water; salty	58
Hydrozincite	B White		72
Jamesonite	B Grey-black	Iridescent metallic	54
Kaolinite	B Earthy grey	Soft plastic clay	113
Leadhillite	B White		69
Lepidolite	B White	Flexible micaceous cleavage	115
Muscovite *	B White	Flexible micaceous cleavage	114
Silver	B Shining grey	Heavy, malleable, metallic	45
Wulfenite	B White		74
Alunite	C White		85
Analcime	C White	Usually in crystal form	112
Anhydrite	C White		83
Barite *	C White	Very heavy for a white mineral	82
Calcite *	C White	Fizzes in dilute HCl	70
Cerussite	C White		73
Colemanite	C White		87
Heulandite	C White	Usually in crystal form	111
Kyanite	C White	Hardness E along one axis	88
Magnesite	C White		73
Manganite	C Reddish-brown or black	Metallic	66
Natrolite	C White	Usually in crystal form	111
Platinum	C Shining light grey	Heavy, malleable, metallic	45
Pyromorphite	C White		77
Scheelite	C White		75
Siderite *	C White		71
Sphalerite *	C Pale-brown		52
Strontianite	C White	Fizzes in dilute HCl	73
Tetrahedrites	C Brown-black		55
Witherite	C White	Fizzes in dilute HCl	71
Wollastonite	C White	Soluble in HCl	97
Anatase	D White	Slightly metallic	62
Arsenopyrite	D Black	Metallic; smells of garlic	54
Cassiterite *	D Dirty white		64
Cobaltite	D Grey-black	Dull metallic	52
Diopside	D Greyish-white	Cleavage at 87° and 93°	101
Leucite	D White		110
Magnetite *	D Black	Strongly magnetic	63
Nepheline	D White		110
Nephrite	D White	Cleavage at 56° and 124°	99
Opal	D White	Iridescent lustre	106
Plagioclase *	D White	Small bladed crystals	108
Psilomelane	D Shining black		65
Pyrolusite	D Black or blue-black		62
Rhodonite	D White	Often black-veined	97
Sodalite	D White		110
Spodumene	D White	Cleavage at 87° and 93°	101
Tremolite	D White	Cleavage at 56° and 124°	99

MINERAL		HARDNESS/STREAK	OTHER FEATURES/PAGE	
Uraninite	D	Black, grey, olive green	Radioactive	67
Zoisite	D	White		93
Axinite	E	White	Wedge-shaped crystals	95
Chrysoberyl	E	Colourless	Crystals often heart-shaped	62
Cordierite	E	Too hard to streak		96
Corundum	E	Colourless		68
Cristobalite	E	White	Octagonal crystals	106
Diamond	E	None	Adamantine lustre	44
Epidote	E	Grey-white	Long, slender striated prisms	93
Quartz *	E	White	Pyramidal crystals	102
Sillimanite	E	White		89
Mercury	–	Not obtainable	Liquid, very heavy	45

ORANGE				
Orpiment	A	Yellow		55
Realgar	A	Orange-yellow		50
Crocoite	B	Orange-yellow		74
Vanadinite	B	White to pale yellow		80
Wulfenite	B	White		74
Mimetite	C	White		77
Pyromorphite	C	White		77
Jadeite	D	White	Cleavage at 87° and 93°	101
Rutile	D	Brown to yellow	Metallic; needle-like	68
Beryl	E	Too hard to streak	Six-sided crystals	96
Diamond	E	None	Adamantine lustre	44
Garnet *	E	White	Noticeably equant grains	90
Quartz *	E	White	Pyramidal crystals	102
Zircon	E	White		92

PINK				
Erythrite	A	Pink to purple		78
Bismuth	B	Silver-white	Metallic; tarnishes	46
Chlorite	B	White	Micaceous cleavage	113
Copper	B	Shining pale red	Heavy, malleable, metallic	46
Hydrozincite	B	White		72
Lepidolite	B	White	Flexible micaceous cleavage	115
Analcime	C	White	Usually in crystal form	112
Apatite	C	White		76
Chabazite	C	White	Usually in crystal form	111
Dolomite *	C	White	Fizzes in dilute HCl	69
Rhodochrosite	C	Pink		72
Smithsonite	C	White		72
Strontianite	C	White	Fizzes in dilute HCl	73
Cobaltite	D	Grey-black	Dull metallic	52
Potash feldspars *	D	White	Twinning common	107
Rhodonite	D	White	Often black-veined	97
Sodalite	D	White		110
Spodumene	D	White	Cleavage at 87° and 93°	101
Tremolite	D	White	Cleavage at 56° and 124°	99
Zoisite	D	White		93
Beryl	E	Too hard to streak	Six-sided crystals	96
Diamond	E	None	Adamantine lustre	44
Garnet *	E	White	Noticeably equant grains	90
Quartz *	E	White	Pyramidal crystals	102
Topaz	E	White		92
Tourmaline *	E	Too hard to streak	Long triangular crystals	95

PURPLE				
Erythrite	A	Pink to purple		78

MINERAL	HARDNESS/STREAK		OTHER FEATURES/PAGE	
Sylvite	A	White	Soluble in water; bitter	60
Bornite	B	Grey-black	Metallic; iridescent	49
Cinnabar	B	Red		53
Hydrozincite	B	White		72
Lepidolite	B	White	Flexible micaceous cleavage	115
Fluorite *	C	White		59
Rhodochrosite	C	Pink		72
Smithsonite	C	White		72
Tetrahedrites	C	Brown-black		55
Anatase	D	White	Slightly metallic	62
Augite	D	Greyish-white	Cleavage at 87° and 93°	101
Cobaltite	D	Grey-black	Dull metallic	52
Jadeite	D	White	Cleavage at 87° and 93°	101
Nephrite	D	White	Cleavage at 56° and 124°	99
Spodumene	D	White	Cleavage at 87° and 93°	101
Tremolite	D	White	Cleavage at 56° and 124°	99
Axinite	E	White	Wedge shaped crystal	95
Cordierite	E	Too hard to streak		96
Corundum	E	Colourless		68
Diamond	E	None	Adamantine lustre	44
Epidote	E	Grey-white	Long, slender striated prisms	93
Garnet *	E	White	Noticeably equant grains	90
Quartz *	E	White	Pyramidal crystals	102

RED				
Gypsum *	A	White		84
Realgar	A	Orange-yellow		50
Stolzite	A	Colourless		75
Sylvite	A	White	Soluble in water; bitter	60
Bornite	B	Grey-black	Metallic; iridescent	49
Cinnabar	B	Red		53
Copper	B	Shining pale red	Heavy, malleable, metallic	46
Crocoite	B	Orange-yellow		74
Halite *	B	White	Soluble in water; salty	58
Proustite	B	Red		55
Pyrargyrite	B	Red	Dull metallic	49
Vanadinite	B	White to pale yellow		80
Alunite	C	White		85
Apatite	C	White		76
Aragonite *	C	White	Fizzes in dilute HCl	71
Calcite *	C	White	Fizzes in dilute HCl	70
Chabazite	C	White	Usually in crystal form	111
Cuprite	C	Shiny brown-red	Dull metallic	64
Fluorite *	C	White		59
Natrolite	C	White	Usually in crystal form	111
Niccolite	C	Brown	Metallic	57
Rhodochrosite	C	Pink		72
Siderite *	C	White		71
Sphalerite *	C	Pale brown		52
Stilbite	C	White	Cruciform penetration twins	112
Brookite	D	White, grey or yellow	Dull metallic	63
Cassiterite *	D	Dirty white		64
Hematite *	D	Red		61
Jadeite	D	White	Cleavage at 87° and 93°	101
Nepheline	D	White		110
Plagioclase *	D	White	Small bladed crystals	108
Potash feldspars *	D	White	Twinning common	107
Rhodonite	D	White	Often black-veined	97
Rutile	D	Brown to yellow	Metallic; needle-like	68

MINERAL	HARDNESS/STREAK		OTHER FEATURES/PAGE	
Axinite	E	White	Wedge shaped crystal	95
Beryl	E	Too hard to streak	Six-sided crystals	96
Corundum	E	Colourless		68
Diamond	E	None	Adamantine lustre	44
Epidote	E	Grey-white	Long, slender striated prisms	93
Garnet *	E	White	Noticeably equant grains	90
Quartz *	E	White	Pyramidal crystals	102
Spinel	E	Colourless	Crystals small, octahedral	67
Tourmaline *	E	Too hard to streak	Long triangular crystals	95
Zircon	E	White		92

WHITE OR COLOURLESS				
Blodite	A	White	Salty	86
Gypsum *	A	White		84
Meyerhofferite	A	White		87
Pyrophillite	A	White		117
Sylvanite	A	White	Bright metallic	56
Sylvite	A	White	Soluble in water; bitter	60
Talc	A	White	Greasy lustre	117
Websterite	A	White	Adheres to tongue	84
Anglesite	B	Grey-white		83
Borax	B	White	Crystals decompose in air	87
Brucite	B	White		67
Chlorargyrite	B	White	Soluble in water	58
Chlorite	B	White	Micaceous cleavage	113
Cryolite	B	White	Powder invisible in water	60
Halite *	B	White	Soluble in water; salty	58
Hydrozincite	B	White		72
Kaolinite	B	Earthy grey	Soft plastic clay	113
Leadhillite	B	White		69
Lepidolite	B	White	Flexible micaceous cleavage	115
Muscovite *	B	White	Flexible micaceous cleavage	114
Thenhardite	B	White	Soluble in water; salty	86
Ulexite	B	White	Soluble in hot water	87
Adamite	C	White		81
Alunite	C	White		85
Analcime	C	White	Usually in crystal form	112
Anhydrite	C	White		83
Antimony	C	Grey	Very dense; metallic	47
Apatite	C	White		76
Apophyllite	C	White	Near cubic crystals	116
Aragonite *	C	White	Fizzes in dilute HCl	71
Arsenic	C	White to grey	Tarnishes; smells of garlic	47
Barite *	C	White	Very heavy for a white mineral	82
Calcite *	C	White	Fizzes in dilute HCl	70
Celestite	C	White	Heavenly blue colour	85
Cerussite	C	White		73
Chabazite	C	White	Usually in crystal form	111
Colemanite	C	White		87
Dolomite *	C	White	Fizzes in dilute HCl	69
Fluorite *	C	White		59
Hemimorphite	C	White		94
Heulandite	C	White	Usually in crystal form	111
Magnesite	C	White		73
Mimetite	C	White		77
Natrolite	C	White	Usually in crystal form	111
Pyromorphite	C	White		77
Scheelite	C	White		75
Scolecite	C	White	Usually in crystal form	112

MINERAL	HARDNESS/STREAK		OTHER FEATURES/PAGE	
Smithsonite	C	White		72
Sphalerite *	C	Pale brown		52
Stilbite	C	White	Cruciform penetration twins	112
Strontianite	C	White	Fizzes in dilute HCl	73
Wavellite	C	White		78
Witherite	C	White	Fizzies in dilute HCl	71
Wollastonite	C	White	Soluble in HCl	97
Amblygonite	D	White		81
Anatase	D	White	Slightly metallic	62
Arsenopyrite	D	Black	Metallic; smells of garlic	54
Cassiterite *	D	Dirty white		64
Leucite	D	White		110
Nepheline	D	White		110
Nephrite	D	White	Cleavage at 56° and 124°	99
Opal	D	White	Iridescent lustre	106
Plagioclase *	D	White	Small bladed crystals	108
Potash feldspars *	D	White	Twinning common	107
Prehnite	D	White	Barrel-like crystals	116
Skutterudite	D	Black	Metallic	54
Sodalite	D	White		110
Spodumene	D	White	Cleavage at 87° and 93°	101
Tremolite	D	White	Cleavage at 56° and 124°	99
Andalusite	E	White		88
Axinite	E	White	Wedge-shaped crystals	95
Beryl	E	Too hard to streak	Six-sided crystals	96
Chrysoberyl	E	Colourless	Crystals often heart-shaped	62
Corundum	E	Colourless		68
Cristobalite	E	White	Octagonal crystals	106
Diamond	E	None	Adamantine lustre	44
Garnet *	E	White	Noticeably equant grains	90
Quartz *	E	White	Pyramidal crystals	102
Sillimanite	E	White		89
Topaz	E	White		92
Tourmaline *	E	Too hard to streak	Long triangular crystals	95
Zircon	E	White		92
Mercury	–	Not obtainable	Liquid, very heavy	45

YELLOW				
Carnotite	A	Yellow	Radioactive	79
Gypsum *	A	White		84
Orpiment	A	Yellow		55
Pyrophillite	A	White		117
Sulphur	A	White		47
Sylvite	A	White	Soluble in water; bitter	60
Autunite	B	Yellow	Radioactive	77
Brucite	B	White		67
Chlorite	B	White	Micaceous cleavage	113
Crocoite	B	Orange-yellow		74
Gold	B	Gold	Malleable, heavy, metallic	44
Halite *	B	White	Soluble in water; salty	58
Hydrozincite	B	White		72
Jarosite	B	Yellow		00
Lepidolite	B	White	Flexible micaceous cleavage	115
Muscovite *	B	White	Flexible micaceous cleavage	114
Phlogopite	B	White	Flexible micaceous cleavage	115
Thenhardite	B	White	Soluble in water; salty	86
Vanadinite	B	White to pale yellow		80
Wulfenite	B	White		74
Xanthophyllite	B	White		115

MINERAL	HARDNESS/STREAK		OTHER FEATURES/PAGE	
Adamite	C	White		81
Alunite	C	White		85
Analcime	C	White	Usually in crystal form	112
Apatite	C	White		76
Apophyllite	C	White	Near cubic crystals	116
Aragonite *	C	White	Fizzes in dilute HCl	71
Calcite *	C	White	Fizzes in dilute HCl	70
Chabazite	C	White	Usually in crystal form	111
Chalcopyrite	C	Greenish-black	Iridescent; metallic	51
Dolomite *	C	White	Fizzes in dilute HCl	69
Fluorite *	C	White		59
Goethite	C	Brownish-yellow		65
Hemimorphite	C	White		94
Heulandite	C	White	Usually in crystal form	111
Magnesite	C	White		73
Millerite	C	Greenish-black	Metallic	54
Mimetite	C	White		77
Monazite	C	White	Radioactive	80
Natrolite	C	White	Usually in crystal form	111
Olivenite	C	Yellow		79
Pyromorphite	C	White		77
Pyrrhotite	C	Grey-black	Metallic; often iridescent	57
Scheelite	C	White		75
Siderite *	C	White		71
Smithsonite *	C	White		72
Sphalerite *	C	Pale brown		52
Stilbite	C	White	Cruciform penetration twins	112
Titanite	C	White	Wedge-shaped crystals	89
Wavellite	C	White		78
Anatase	D	White	Slightly metallic	62
Cassiterite *	D	Dirty white		64
Enstatite	D	Greyish-white	Cleavage at 87° and 93°	100
Jadeite	D	White	Cleavage at 87° and 93°	101
Marcasite *	D	Greenish-black	Metallic when fresh	53
Nepheline	D	White		110
Opal	D	White	Iridescent lustre	106
Potash feldspars *	D	White	Twinning common	107
Pyrite *	D	Greenish-black	Bright metallic	48
Rhodonite	D	White	Often black-veined	97
Rutile	D	Brown to yellow	Metallic; needle-like	68
Sodalite	D	White		110
Spodumene	D	White	Cleavage at 87° and 93°	101
Tremolite	D	White	Cleavage at 56° and 124°	99
Beryl	E	Too hard to streak	Six-sided crystals	96
Chrysoberyl	E	Colourless	Crystals often heart-shaped	62
Corundum	E	Colourless		68
Cristobalite	E	White		106
Diamond	E	None	Octagonal crystals	44
Epidote	E	Grey-white	Adamantine lustre	93
Garnet *	E	White	Long, slender striated prisms	90
Olivine *	E	White	Noticeably equant grains	89
Quartz *	E	White	Pyramidal crystals	102
Sillimanite	E	White		89
Topaz	E	White		92
Vesuvianite	E	White	Prismatic crystals	94
Zircon	E	White		92

Native elements

The members of this group are all highly distinctive and very rare, forming just a tiny fraction of the minerals found on Earth. Their rarity can be explained by considering their chemical characteristics. Elements are made up of just one type of atom; this is in contrast to most naturally-occurring materials, which are chemical compounds. All atoms are composed of protons and neutrons (the nucleus), and a number of electrons arranged in a precise sequence of "shells" around the nucleus. Each of these shells can accommodate a particular number of electrons; and if a shell lacks a full complement, it shares its electrons with another atom of a different element. This more stable configuration is known as a chemical compound.

Some elements already have shells that are completely filled with electrons; all of these are highly stable gases, such as helium and argon. However, most have partly-filled shells and combine rapidly to form compounds. Even the elements described in this section, which do occur naturally as minerals, form compounds with water and oxygen soon after their extraction from the ground, and they exist by themselves only in conditions where suitable "mates" are absent. They are usually found in and around igneous rocks, frequently deep underground. Most are malleable metals, and have a shiny metallic lustre.

Gold

Au
H. 2.5–3: S.G. 19.3
Cubic. Hydrothermal veins and placers
Golden-yellow, silver-white or orange-red. Metallic and opaque. Does not tarnish. Streak golden-yellow and shiny. Usually occurs as grains, nuggets, sheets, flakes or wires. Crystals rare, usually small octahedrons. Bends easily and can be cut with a knife.
Used as a monetary standard, in jewellery and dentistry.

Diamond

C
H. 10: S.G. 3.5
Cubic. Kimberlite pipes and placers
Colourless, white, grey, yellow, brown, orange, pink, lavender, blue, green or black, but rarer in darker colours. Transparent or translucent with a greasy lustre, like oiled glass. Crystals usually octahedral, with curved crystal faces, but also found as rounded grains. The hardest known mineral, it is used in jewellery.

Silver

Ag
H 2.5–3; S.G 10.5
Cubic. Veins and volcanic rocks
Silver-white when fresh, but tarnishes easily to brown, yellow, grey or black. Opaque and metallic with a grey, shining streak. Found as irregular masses, or branched or wire-like forms. Crystals rare, usually groups of parallel cubes. Bends easily and can be cut with a knife. Used extensively in the manufacture of photographic emulsions, also for coinage, jewellery and electronic circuits.

Platinum *(not shown)*

Pt
H. 4–4.5; S.G. 14–21
Cubic. Silica-poor rocks and placers
Silver- to steel-grey, metallic and opaque. Streak steel-grey. Does not tarnish. Usually found as small grains or nuggets, rarely as deformed cubic crystals. Bends easily and is weakly magnetic. Used in jewellery, chemical and electrical equipment.

Mercury *(not shown)*

Hg
S.G. 13.6
Volcanic environments
The only native element that is liquid at room temperature. It crystallizes at −39° C into the hexagonal system. Silver-white, metallic, opaque. Used in the recovery of gold and silver, and in the production of pharmaceuticals.

Graphite
C

H. 1–2: S.G. 2.2
Hexagonal. Metamorphic rocks
Black or grey-black, opaque, with a grey-black streak. Shiny-wet lustre, greasy feel. Occurs in foliated masses, scales or thin plates. Perfect cleavage. Flexible, and can be cut with a knife. Graphite leaves a grey stain on the fingers. Used as the "lead" in pencils, as electrodes (it is a good electrical conductor) and as a dry lubricant. Easily confused with molybdenite, but is darker.

Copper
Cu

H. 2.5–3; S.G. 8.9
Cubic. Widespread occurrence
Rose-pink when completely fresh, but tarnishes quickly to copper-red and brown. Can be iridescent, but more frequently covered by a green, blue or blackish film. Metallic and opaque, with a shiny and copper-red streak. Can be cut with a knife and bent easily. Usually found in irregular, sometimes branching, masses. Crystals rare, cubic and often distorted. An excellent conductor of both electricity and heat, it is used to make cables and alloys, such as brass.

Bismuth
Bi

H. 2–2.5; S.G. 9.8
Trigonal. Hydrothermal veins
Silver-white or grey with a pinkish tinge. Shining silver streak. Metallic, iridescent when tarnished, opaque. Usually massive, sometimes granular or lamellar. Can be cut with a knife, but is brittle. Good cleavage.

Arsenic

As

H.3.5: S.G. 5.7

Trigonal. Hydrothermal veins
Silvery-white when fresh,
tarnishes to dark grey. Metallic
lustre, grey streak. Weathers to a
black crust. Usually massive and
granular, with concentric
layering visible, but can be
reniform or stalactitic. Single
crystals rare, needle-like with
one perfect cleavage. Brittle with
uneven fracture. Smells of garlic.
Similar to antimony and often
found with it in association with
silver, nickel and cobalt ores.

Sulphur

S

H. 1.5–2.5: S.G. 2

*Orthorhombic. Volcanic
environments and evaporites*
This distinctive mineral is
characteristically bright yellow,
but can be orange, red, brown,
green, grey or black if impurities
are present. Commonly occurs
as crystals, also in granular
aggregates. Gives a white streak.
Greasy lustre, translucent to
transparent. Burns easily with a
blue flame and a distinctive "bad
egg" smell. Used in the
manufacture of acid, gunpowder,
fertilizers and matches.

Antimony

Sb

H. 3–3.5: S.G. 6.7

Trigonal. Hydrothermal veins
Silvery-white to grey, bright
metallic lustre, opaque; streak
light grey. Soft, usually massive,
sometimes with a radiating
pattern. Antimony crystals have
one good cleavage and are very
brittle. Often found with stibnite
and other sulphides. Very
uncommon.

Sulphides

The sulphide minerals are all heavy and usually have a metallic lustre. They tarnish easily, sometimes becoming iridescent. They are usually opaque and have a coloured streak. Frequently found in hydrothermal veins, they include many valuable ores. Some of the sulphide ores, most notably galena and the copper sulphides, have long been exploited due to the ease with which the metals could be separated from the sulphur by the process of smelting. Copper sulphides have been mined for well over two millennia in areas like Cornwall (southern UK), though most mines were opened up after the onset of the industrial revolution. The spoil heaps of abandoned mines offer fertile ground for the mineral collector.

A

Pyrite

FeS$_2$
H. 6–6.5: S.G. 5.0
Cubic. Hydrothermal veins, pegmatites, silica-poor lavas and deep seated intrusions, metamorphic and sedimentary rocks

Often known as fool's gold because of its golden colour, pyrite is the most widespread and abundant sulphide mineral. It is easily distinguished from gold by its greater hardness and brittleness. Although some pyrite is golden, it can vary in colour from pale brass to dark yellowy-brown. All colours have a greenish-black streak. It tarnishes gradually when exposed to air or water, either at the surface of the Earth or underground; the mineral becomes coated with a brown film, which is sometimes iridescent. When fresh, pyrite has a bright, metallic lustre. It is always opaque. Crystals are cubic or octahedral, and usually intergrown, often into complex shapes (A). Crystal faces are commonly striated. Frequently found massive, as granular aggregates. Also occurs disseminated through the rock, sometimes replacing fossil skeletons. Pyrite has no modern commercial use.

Enargite

Cu₃AsS₄
H. 3: S.G. 4.4
Orthorhombic. Hydrothermal veins

Black or grey with a black streak. Opaque with a metallic lustre. Tabular or prismatic crystals, which may be striated. Perfect cleavage. Usually found in bladed or granular masses. A moderately important ore of copper and arsenic.

Chalcocite

Cu₂S
H. 2.5–3: S.G. 5.5–5.8
Orthorhombic. Hydrothermal veins

Blackish-grey to black, with a shining dark grey streak. Tarnishes rapidly to dull black or green. Bright metallic lustre when fresh. Can just about be cut with a knife. Often massive or disseminated through the rock. Single crystals, when present, are prismatic or tabular and striated on one face. An important ore of copper.

Bornite

Cu₅FeS₄
H. 3: S.G. 5.1
Cubic. Hydrothermal veins, metamorphic rock, pegmatites

Fresh surfaces are red or bronze, tarnishing to iridescent purple, blue or red. Metallic lustre, grey-black streak. Usually found in compact, granular masses. Crystals rare, often with rough, curved faces. An ore of copper.

Pyrargyrite

Ag₃SbS₃
H. 2.5: S.G. 5.9
Trigonal. Hydrothermal veins

Black-red with a dark cherry-red streak. Translucent, with a greasy or dull metallic lustre. Crystals are prismatic and striated, with one distinct cleavage. Also found massive, in crusts, or disseminatd throughout the rock. A minor silver ore.

A

B

Galena

PbS
H. 2.5: S.G. 7.6
Cubic. Hydrothermal veins,
especially where these pass
through limestones; sedimentary
and metamorphic deposits,
occasionally pegmatites
Lead to silver-grey, with a dark
grey streak. Bright metallic lustre
when fresh but tarnishes to a
dull grey. Common as cubic,
often intergrown, crystals (A),
but can be dodecahedral (B).
Also found as massive deposits.
Both masses and crystals have
three perfect cleavages. Often
found in veins or lodes in
association with sphalerite,
chalcopyrite, pyrite, barite,
calcite, fluorite and quartz.

Galena is a principal ore of
lead, yielding up to 1 kg per
tonne. Lead is used in storage
batteries, solder and a variety of
alloys.

Realgar

AsS
H. 1.5–2: S.G. 3.6
Monoclinic. Hot springs and
hydrothermal veins
Dark red to orange. Streak
orange-yellow. Loses colour and
becomes powdery on exposure
to light and air. Translucent to
transparent with a greasy lustre.
Crystals short, prismatic and
striated, with four indistinct
cleavages.

Chalcopyrite

CuFeS$_2$
H. 3.5–4: S.G. 4.2
Tetragonal. Hydrothermal veins,
contact metamorphic rocks,
silica-poor magmas and placer
deposits

One of the most widely
distributed of the copper
minerals. Distinctive deep brass-
yellow colour when fresh. Streak
greenish-black. Often tarnishes
to an iridescent brassy colour
(A). Opaque with a metallic
lustre. Crystals (A and B) often
have rounded faces that are
striated in several directions.
More commonly massive (C),
granular or disseminated
throughout the rock. Similar to
pyrite but softer and can be
scratched with a knife. Crystals
are less regular than those of
pyrite. Both these minerals can
be confused with gold, but are
distinguished by their brittleness
and lighter weight. About 80%
of the world's copper is derived
from chalcopyrite; gold and
silver are by-products of its
processing. Chalcopyrite often
occurs with pyrite, galena,
sphalerite, chalcocite, malachite,
calcite and quartz.

Bismuthinite

Bi$_2$S$_3$
H. 2: S.G. 6.8
Orthorhombic. Hydrothermal
veins and pegmatites

Lead-grey, with a lead-grey
streak. Tarnishes yellow or
iridescent. Opaque, with a
metallic lustre. Most commonly
found massive, foliated or
fibrous. Crystals are long and
prismatic, or even needle-like
and have vertical striations
down their faces. Crystals are
flexible, and both crystals and
masses can just be cut with a
knife. One perfect cleavage. The
best ore of bismuth. Could be
confused with galena, but is
much softer; could also be
mistaken for stibnite, but is
much heavier.

Sphalerite
ZnS
H. 3.5–4; S.G. 4
Cubic. Hydrothermal veins, especially where these pass through limestones. Pegmatites, sedimentary and metamorphic rocks
Usually blackish-red or brown, but can also be yellow, green, red, grey or colourless. Streak pale brown or white. Can be translucent or even transparent when in thin sections. Most often it is slightly translucent. A reddish tinge at the edges of crystals is characteristic. All crystals have a greasy lustre, and are often tetrahedral with rounded faces. One perfect cleavage. Also forms masses, which can be granular, botryoidal or stalactitic. In vein environments it is commonly associated with galena, chalcopyrite, barite, fluorite, quartz and calcite. Sphalerite is the main ore of zinc, which is used in alloys.

Cobaltite
CoAsS
H. 5.5; S.G. 6.3
Cubic. Hydrothermal veins and regional metamorphic rock
Light to dark grey with a pink or violet tinge. Streak greyish-black. Bright or dull metallic lustre, opaque. Usually occurs as crystals, but may be massive.

Molybdenite
MoS₂
H. 1–1.5; S.G. 4.7
Hexagonal. Widespread
Blue-grey, with a blue-grey to greenish streak. Metallic to greasy lustre, opaque. Cuts with a knife. Crystals tabular and flexible. Commonly occurs as scales or foliated masses.

Covellite
CuS
H. 1.5–2: S.G. 4.7
Hexagonal. Hydrothermal veins and volcanic environments
Very dark, indigo in colour, often with an iridescent tarnish. Shining grey-black streak. Dull metallic or dull lustre. Usually massive and foliated. Crystals are thin, flexible, hexagonal plates. Cleavage perfect. A minor ore of copper.

Cinnabar
HgS
H. 2–2.5: S.G. 8.1
Trigonal. Hydrothermal veins and volcanic hot springs
Bright red or pink-red, can be purplish or brownish. Streak scarlet to red-brown. Transparent to translucent, greasy lustre, but often earthy. Usually massive or fine grained. Crystals rare, rhombohedral or tabular with perfect cleavage. The principal ore of mercury.

Marcasite
FeS₂

FeS$_2$
H. 6–6.5: S.G. 4.9
Orthorhombic. Low-temperature hydrothermal veins and sedimentary rocks, especially shales, clays and limestones
Pale, brassy yellow, sometimes with a greenish tinge, to almost white. Greenish-black streak. Metallic to earthy, opaque. Tarnishes to a deeper yellow or brown, and decomposes on prolonged exposure to air, forming a white powder. Crystals often twinned, coxcomb or spear shaped. Common as radiating masses and nodules with brown, reniform crusts. Often occurs in association with galena, sphalerite, calcite, dolomite and clay minerals. Similar to pyrite, with the same chemical components, but is whiter and has a distinctive crystal shape. No commercial uses.

Arsenopyrite

FeAsS
H. 5.5–6: S.G. 6.1
Monoclinic. Hydrothermal veins
Silver-white to steel-grey with a
black streak. Metallic lustre,
opaque, good cleavage. Stubby,
prismatic crystals with striations
on the sides. Crystal shape is the
best field characteristic for the
identification of this mineral.
Also found as granular masses.
Sometimes smells of garlic.
Produces sparks when struck
with a hammer. The principal
ore of arsenic and sometimes
mined for its gold content.

Millerite

NiS
H. 3–3.5: S.G. 5.4
*Trigonal. Hydrothermal veins
and limestones.*
Brassy-yellow with a greenish
tinge. Greenish-black streak.
Opaque and metallic. Needle-
like crystals frequently occur in
radiating "tufts". Massive
millerite can form crusts (as
shown), which have a velvety
texture. Most frequently found
in limestone cavities in
association with hematite and
siderite. This rare mineral is a
rich ore of nickel.

Jamesonite

$Pb_4FeSb_6S_{14}$
H. 2.5: S.G. 5.6
Monoclinic. Hydrothermal veins
Grey-black, with a streak of the
same colour. Tarnishes to
iridescence. Metallic and
opaque. Crystals have a
distinctive appearance – either
loosely-matted and needle-like
or brittle and feathery. Crystals
are striated on their long axis
with good cleavage across this
direction. Similar to
boulangerite, but crystals of
jamesonite are brittle. A minor
lead ore, often found in
association with gold, quartz
and the tetrahedrites.

Skutterudite

(Co, Ni)As₃
H. 5.5–6: S.G. 6.1–6.9
Cubic. Hydrothermal veins
A series of minerals containing
varying amounts of nickel and
cobalt. Cobalt-rich forms are
known as skutterudite, nickel-
rich forms are technically
cloanthite. Iron-white with a
black streak. Sometimes
tarnishes to grey or iridescent.
Metallic lustre, opaque. Cubic or
octahedral crystals with perfect
cleavage; also massive, when it is
compact and granular. Brittle
when hit. Uncommon, but a
moderately important ore of
cobalt, arsenic and nickel.

Proustite
Ag₃AsS₃
H. 2–2.5; S.G. 5.6
Trigonal. Hydrothermal veins
One of the most beautiful of the sulphide minerals. Bright, shining red, which darkens after exposure to light. Scarlet streak. Translucent to transparent with a submetallic to greasy lustre. Usually occurs massive or disseminated through the rock. When crystals occur they are prismatic with a hexagonal base, with one distinct cleavage. A minor ore of silver.

Boulangerite
Pb₅Sb₄S₁₁
H. 2.5–3; S.G. 6.2
Monoclinic. Hydrothermal veins
Grey to bluish-grey, with a brownish streak. Dull metallic lustre, opaque, good cleavage. Commonly occurs in fibrous masses, as needle-like crystals or fibrous plumes. The fibres are flexible, which distinguishes this mineral from jamesonite. One of the ores of lead.

Orpiment
As₂S₃
H. 1.5–2; SG. 3.5
Monoclinic. Low-temperature hydrothermal veins and hot springs
Lemon-yellow to golden-orange, with a lemon-yellow streak. Transparent to translucent, greasy lustre, pearly on cleavage planes. Crumbles when exposed to light and air. Short, prismatic crystals with perfect cleavage. Splits into thin, flexible flakes. Can just be cut with a knife. An ore of arsenic.

Tetrahedrite group
(Cu,Fe)₁₂Sb₄S₁₃ – (Cu, Fe)₁₂As₄S₁₃
H. 3–4.5; S.G. 4.5–5.2
Cubic. Hydrothermal veins
A set of minerals including tetrahedrite (shown here) and tennantite, which have similar properties. Dark grey, black or brown, rarely purple or dark blue, with a brown or black streak. Opaque and metallic. Crystals rare, tetrahedral. More commonly found in compact or granular masses. Brittle, with an uneven fracture.

Bournonite

PbCuSbS₃
H. 2.5–3: S.G. 5.8
Orthorhombic. Hydrothermal veins

Steel- or dark lead-grey to iron-black in colour. Streak is grey or black and varies with the colour of the mineral. Opaque, with a metallic lustre. Has two poorer cleavages at right angles to one good cleavage. Crystals are tabular or stubby prisms. Sometimes called cogwheel ore, as it can be found as sets of crystals twinned into cogwheel-shaped groups. Also found massive and granular. A minor ore of copper, lead and antimony. Most often found in association with galena.

Sylvanite

AgAuTe₄
H. 1.5–2: S.G.8.2
Monoclinic. Hydrothermal veins

A silver-white mineral with a silver-white streak. Always opaque, with a bright metallic lustre. Crystals are variable in shape, but usually stubby prisms. More commonly massive or branching; branches sometimes resemble written characters, giving it the name "graphic ore". An ore of gold, silver and tellurium. It is found in association with quartz, acanthite, pyrite, fluorite and rhodochrosite.

Pyrrhotite

Fe₁₋ₓS
H. 3.5-4.5: S.G. 4.6
Hexagonal. Silica-poor plutons, metamorphic rocks and hydrothermal veins
Bronze-red to bronze-yellow, often tarnished brown and sometimes iridescent. Streak grey-black. Opaque, with a bright metallic lustre. Often highly magnetic. Usually massive, or granular. Single crystals are tabular, with striations on their faces. Breaks with an uneven fracture. No cleavage. Not a useful ore of iron, but large pyrrhotite masses often contain ores of other elements.

Stibnite

Sb₂S₃
H. 2: S.G. 4.7
Orthorhombic. Hydrothermal veins and hot springs
Light to dark grey with a streak of the same colour. Often tarnished to dark iridescence. Brilliant metallic lustre, opaque. Crystals needle-like or long prisms, striated vertically. Can occur in felted, granular or compact masses. Sometimes shows red or orange alteration.

Niccolite

NiAs
H. 5-5.5: S.G. 7.8
Hexagonal. Hydrothermal veins

Also known as nickeline. Pale coppery-red, with a brownish streak. Tarnishes readily to grey or black. Opaque, metallic lustre. Usually occurs as masses, which can be kidney shaped or columnar. Crystals rare, small and pyramidal, and often distorted. The first nickel ore, and still used as one when sufficient quantities are available.

Halides

Many of the halide minerals dissolve in water and have a distinctive salty taste. They are usually soft, translucent or transparent, with a relatively low specific gravity. A large number of them crystallize in the cubic system. Many halides form on the surface of the Earth, being deposited in lakes and seas from which water evaporates faster than it can be replaced. A distinctive suite of minerals forms from sea water, and another from fresh water. Impurities in the water system give rise to some of the rarer halides.

Halite
NaCl
H. 2.5: S.G. 2.2
Cubic. Evaporitic environments
Rock salt is colourless or white, with tints of grey, yellow, red or blue. It has a white streak, glassy lustre and perfect cubic cleavage. Translucent to transparent. Crystals often show facial depressions. Dissolves readily in water and has a characteristic salty taste. Found in large deposits, often in conjunction with gypsum and anhydrite. Halite often occurs in beds interspersed with other sediments. When buried by deposition, it is put under pressure and can flow like a viscous liquid, albeit very slowly. Under certain conditions, it flows into "salt domes", which bulge up towards the surface. It is the chief source of culinary salt and an important source of both sodium and chlorine.

Chlorargyrite
AgCl
H. 2.5: S.G. 5.6
Cubic. Hydrothermal veins
Colourless or grey when fresh, but darkens to violet, purple or brown on exposure to light. Translucent with a waxy lustre and a white streak. Crystals rare; usually found massive or as crusts. Forms by the alteration of other silver minerals. Can be cut with a knife.

Fluorite

CaF₂

H. 4: S.G 3.2

Cubic. Varied environments

A common mineral, which occurs in many colours. Violet-purple, green, blue, yellow, rose, red, white and colourless are the most frequently encountered. White streak and glassy lustre, translucent to transparent. Crystals are never perfect cubes. They always grow in the form of interlocking twins. This habit is particularly well developed in the specimens marked B and C. Cleavage good in three direction, which are at right angles to each other. Cleavage planes can often be seen inside the crystals; they appear as white planes (visible in specimens labelled A and C).

Fluorite is found in granular masses as well as in crystal form. Occurs commonly in hydrothermal veins in association with metallic sulphide ores, barite, calcite, dolomite and quartz. It can also occur in contact metamorphic zones and as an accessory mineral in igneous rocks. Used as a flux in the smelting of iron and other metals, and in the manufacture of hydrofluoric acid.

59

Sylvite

KCl
H. 2: S.G. 2
Cubic. Evaporitic environments
White or colourless to pinky-red.
The red colouration is due to the
presence of hematite impurities.
May also be blue, purple, yellow
or grey. White streak, glassy
lustre. Transparent to
translucent. Commonly found as
cubic or octahedral crystals, as
well as fine-grained masses and
coarser aggregates. Dissolves in
water. Found in conjunction
with halite with which it is easily
confused. May be distinguished
by its more bitter taste.
Sometimes used as a fertilizer.

Cryolite

Na₃AlF₆
H. 2.5: S.G. 3.0
Monoclinic. Granitic pegmatites
White or colourless. Translucent
with a white streak and waxy
lustre. Usually found massive,
but breaks up to resemble cubes,
although it has no cleavage.
Often found in association with
brown siderite. This rare mineral
occurs in commercially
significant quantities only in
Greenland. Used as a catalyst in
the smelting of aluminium. An
unusual property of the
powdered mineral is that it is
almost invisible when put into
water.

Oxides and hydroxides

This large and variable group includes many gemstones and important ore minerals. The oxides and hydroxides are generally resistant to alteration because of the strong chemical bonds that form between oxygen and other elements. They form a diverse group of minerals which have few properties in common. They are generally hard, most scoring at least 5 on Mohs' scale. Colour, streak, lustre and specific gravity vary widely.

Hematite

Fe_2O_3
H. 5.5-6.5: S.G. 5.3
Trigonal. Common in igneous rocks, pegmatites and hydrothermal veins. Found in deposits of sedimentary origin. Found in two distinct habits. Most commonly red to red-brown with a red streak, occuring in non-crystalline aggregates. These vary widely, but are frequently botryoidal or kidney-shaped (when it is known as kidney ore). Metallic or earthy lustre, opaque. More rarely occurs in crystals which are black, opaque and very shiny with a metallic lustre and red or brown streak (specular hematite). Can form beds up to 300 m thick in sedimentary rocks, making it the most important ore of iron. Also used as a red pigment and as a polishing powder.

Chrysoberyl

BeAl$_2$O$_4$
H. 8.5: S.G. 3.7
Orthorhombic. Pegmatites and metamorphic rocks
Colourless, green, brown, grey or yellow. Green specimens sometimes appear red under artificial light (especially variety alexandrite). Too hard to give a streak; transparent to translucent with a glassy lustre. Crystals usually tabular or stubby prisms, often twinned and heart shaped. Crystals are striated with several fairly poor cleavages. Also occurs in granular masses. Some varieties of chrysoberyl are used as gemstones.

Pyrolusite

MnO$_2$
H. 2: S.G. 5.0
Tetragonal. Hydrothermal veins and sedimentary rocks
Black or blue steel-grey with a black or blue-black streak. Opaque, metallic to dull lustre. Crystalline form (which is called polianite) is rare; prismatic with one perfect cleavage. More commonly occurs as earthy masses or concretions, which can be fibrous or dendritic. A commercially-significant ore of manganese.

Anatase

TiO$_2$
H. 5.5–6: S.G. 3.9
Tetragonal. Widespread occurrence
Commonly in the colour range brown-black to blue-black, but can also be colourless, yellow, grey, green or pale purple. White streak. Transparent to almost opaque, with a greasy or slightly metallic lustre. Crystals are usually striated tall pyramids with perfect cleavage. Brittle, with a slightly curved fracture. An infrequent ore of titanium.

Brookite
TiO$_2$
H. 5.5– 6: S.G. 4.1
Orthorhombic. Widespread occurrence

Brown, red-brown or black, with a streak that is white, sometimes slightly grey or yellow. Specimens are transparent to opaque, with a greasy or slightly metallic lustre. Always crystalline, commonly with tabular or diamond-shaped striated crystals. Brittle, with an uneven fracture and indistinct cleavage. Brookite is potentially valuable as an ore of titanium, but is rarely found in sufficient quantities to make mining economically viable.

Magnetite
Fe$_3$O$_4$
H. 5.5–6.5: S.G. 5.2
Cubic. Widespread occurrence

Dark grey-black or iron-black, with a black streak. Always opaque, even in thin slices. When fresh, it has a bright metallic lustre, but rapidly tarnishes to dull, occasionally to iridescent, on contact with air. Magnetite is strongly magnetic. It was used as a lodestone and in the first compasses made by the Chinese. Crystals are octahedral or dodecahedral and often have striated faces; lamellar twins occur. There is no cleavage, but partings do occur parallel to the octahedral crystal faces. The mineral is often found in granular masses. It is always brittle, breaking with a slightly conchoidal fracture.

Magnetite is a common accessory mineral in a variety of silica-poor magmas. In gabbros, it crystallizes early in the cooling and sinks to the floor of the magma chamber where it accumulates in layers. It is resistant to weathering and is a common constituent of sedimentary rocks such as sandstone. Also found in metamorphic rocks and hydrothermal veins. It is the richest and most important ore of iron when it occurs in large enough quantities. Can be confused with ilmenite, but has a darker streak.

Cuprite

Cu₂O
H. 3.5–4: S.G. 6.2
Cubic. Hydrothermal veins
Dark red to ruby-red in colour,
with an unusually shiny
brownish-red streak. When
fresh, it is translucent to
transparent, but becomes almost
opaque (as shown here) after
exposure to air. It has a variable
lustre that depends on habit.
Crystals are greasy or slightly
metallic, but crusts and massive
specimens tend to be earthy.
Crystals are usually octahedrons
or cubes, but can be
dodecahedral. Also occurs as
hair-like aggregates and mats
(when it is known as
chalcotrichite). Cuprite forms
when other copper minerals are
altered by water at near-surface
temperatures.

Cassiterite

SnO₂
H. 6–7: S.G. 7.0
*Tetragonal. Hydrothermal veins,
pegmatites and placers*
Usually brown to black in
colour, but can be colourless,
grey, yellow, green or red. Streak
is a dirty white or light brown.
Transparent to almost opaque
with a variable, but often greasy,
lustre. Short, prismatic crystals
occur, but it is more usually
massive, granular or
disseminated through the rock.
Also found in kidney-shaped
lumps filled with radiating
fibres, when it is known as
wood-tin. One of the principal
ores of tin.

Goethite
FeO(OH)
H. 5–5.5: S.G. 3.3–4.3
Orthorhombic. Hydrothermal veins, sediments and soils
Yellow-brown to black in colour, with a brownish-yellow streak. Translucent to opaque. Lustre silky and varnish-like, but can be earthy. Crystals rare, it is more usually botryoidal, with a radial, fibrous centre. In the specimen shown, the crystals occur in a skeletal latticework of quartz deposited in a hydrothermal environment. Also found as soft earthy masses. Goethite is an important iron ore in some parts of the world, particularly Europe. It is often found in association with quartz and calcite.

Chromite
FeCr₂O₄
H 5.5: S.G. 4.5–4.8
Cubic. Silica-poor igneous rocks and placers
Black with a brown streak. Opaque with a metallic lustre. Usually massive, compact or granular, or disseminated through the rock. When crystals occur they are octahedral and less than 1 cm long. Brittle, with an uneven fracture and no cleavage. Sometimes weakly magnetic. The main ore of chromium, which is used in alloys, chrome plating and leather tanning.

Psilomelane
$BaMn^{2+}Mn^{4+}{}_8O_{16}(OH)_4$
H. 5–6: S.G. 3.7–4.7
Orthorhombic: Sedimentary rocks
Black or dark grey with a black, shining streak. Opaque, with a metallic to dull lustre. Never found as crystals. Its most common occurrence is as a tree-like growth on flat planes in sedimentary rocks. Also occurs as black aggregates and masses.

Manganite

MnO(OH)
H. 4: S.G. 4.3
Monoclinic. Hydrothermal veins, soils and sedimentary rocks
Black to grey with a reddish-brown or black streak. Opaque when thick, but translucent in thin slices. Has a metallic or submetallic lustre. Crystals are striated, long prisms which are often twinned or occur in bundles. There are three cleavages, one perfect and two poor. Most commonly massive and concretionary. Often found in association with quartz, galena, pyrolusite, cinnabar and acanthite.

Columbite-tantalite group

(Fe,Mn)(Nb,Ta)₂O₆
(Fe,Mn)(Nb,Ta)$_2$O$_6$
H. 6: S.G. 5.3–8.1
Orthorhombic. Pegmatites and placers
Black to reddish-brown, with a black or dark red streak. Often tarnishes to iridescence. Opaque, slightly metallic or glassy lustre. Most minerals of this series have at least small amounts of all the elements in the formula, pure end-members are rare. Density of the mineral increases with the tantalum (Ta) content. Crystals can be tabular or stubby prisms (such as the specimen shown here) or rarely pyramidal. Heart-shaped twins are common. Crystals are often striated and have triangular marks. This group of minerals forms an important ore of tantalum and niobium, both of which are rare elements. Can occur as large aggregates of crystals, or in compact masses.

Ilmenite

FeTiO₃
FeTiO$_3$
H. 5-6: S.G. 4.7
Trigonal. Igneous and metamorphic rocks, pegmatites and placers
Black, with a red alteration product quickly forming on exposed surfaces. Black streak. Opaque, metallic when fresh but tarnishing to a dull lustre. Occurs as thick, tabular crystals, also as grains and masses. Brittle.

Spinel

MgAl₂O₄
H. 7.5–8; S.G. 3.5–4.1
Cubic. Metamorphic rocks and placers.

May be black or brown (when it is called picotite), green (pleonaste), blue or red. Streak colour is similarly variable. Transparent to opaque with a glassy to dull lustre. The most common crystals are small, perfect octahedrons. Massive aggregates and rounded grains are also frequently found. Transparent varieties of all colours are used as gems.

Brucite

Mg(OH)₂
H. 2.5; S.G. 2.4
Trigonal. Metamorphic rocks

White, pale green, blue, grey, pinky-yellow or dark brown with a white streak. Transparent to translucent, waxy or glassy lustre, pearly on cleavage surfaces. Crystals broad and tabular with a perfect cleavage. Plates are easily separated and flexible, and they can be cut with a knife. Usually massive or fibrous, when it is one of the varieties of asbestos. Occurs in fibres up to 2m long.

Uraninite

UO₂
H. 5–6; S.G. 7.5–10
Cubic. Hydrothermal veins, pegmatites and sedimentary rocks

Black, sometimes greyish- or brownish-black. Variable streak, may be black, grey-black or olive green. Usually opaque with a slightly metallic or greasy lustre. Crystals are usually cubic and can occur in branching aggregates. Good cleavage can be seen in polished sections. Commonly massive, with a fibrous to columnar structure (when it is known as pitchblende). This form is softer, with a hardness of about 4.4. Both forms are highly radioactive, and are important uranium ores.

Corundum

Al₂O₃
H. 9; S.G. 4
Trigonal. Pegmatites and metamorphic rocks

Gem varieties of corundum are red ruby and blue sapphire. Usually coloured grey or brown, but can also be red, blue, yellow, green, purple, colourless or even multi-coloured. Red and grey varieties are shown here. Corundum is the reference mineral that sets hardness 9 on Mohs' scale; it is too hard to give a streak. Transparent to translucent with a glassy lustre. Crystals are common and often large, with a highly variable form, frequently pyramidal with hexagonal bases, and sometimes deeply furrowed or striated. Corundum is similar in appearance to some feldspars, but it is much harder. Often found with albite and members of the garnet group.

A

Rutile

TiO₂
H. 6–6.5; S.G. 4.3
Tetragonal. Widespread occurrence

A variably coloured mineral. Most often brown or reddish, but can also be yellow, orange, blue, grey or black. The streak is consistently brown or yellow. Usually opaque, but lighter colours can be translucent or transparent. All colours have a metallic or greasy lustre. The most characteristic habit is long, thin, needle-like crystals, typically thinner than specimen A. These needles often grow inside quartz, when they are known as "maiden's hair". Stubby, prismatic crystals (B) are also common; they are fragile with two good cleavages and one poor, and are often twinned into a bent-knee shape. Rutile is an important ore of titanium.

B

Carbonates

These minerals are often soft, usually light coloured, and have a low specific gravity. Most release carbon dioxide gas when placed in contact with dilute hydrochloric acid. The "fizzing" as gas is released is a useful diagnostic property. Carbonates are widespread in occurrence, and can form in surface environments as well as deep underground. Calcite, aragonite and dolomite are common constituents of limestones, and most fossils are composed of these minerals.

Malachite

$Cu_2CO_3(OH)_2$
H. 3.5-4: S.G. 4.0
Monoclinic. Hydrothermal veins and sedimentary rocks
Various shades of green, with a pale green streak. Crystals needle-like or long prisms, translucent to transparent with a glassy lustre. Usually massive, or found as a crust with a botryoidal surface. Often fibrous.

Leadhillite

$Pb_4SO_4(CO_3)_2(OH)_2$
H. 2.5-3: S.G. 6.6
Monoclinic. Hydrothermal veins
Colourless, white, grey, sometimes tinged yellow, green or blue. Streak white. Translucent or transparent, with a resinous or greasy lustre. Just cuts with a knife.

Dolomite

$CaMg(CO_3)_2$
H. 3.5-4: S.G. 2.9
Hexagonal. Sedimentary and metamorphic rocks
Very common. Colourless, white, pink or yellow, with a white streak. Transparent to opaque, with a glassy or pearly lustre. Crystals are usually simple rhombs. Most frequent as massive, granular aggregates.

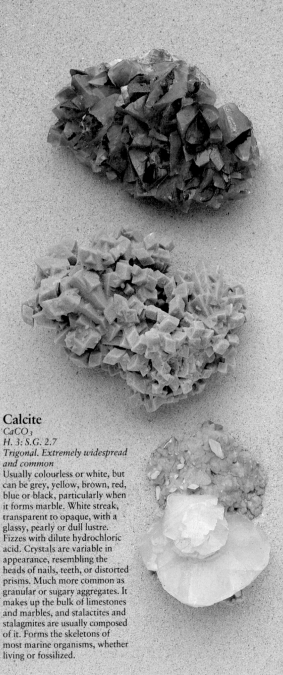

Calcite

CaCO₃

H. 3: S.G. 2.7

Trigonal. Extremely widespread and common

Usually colourless or white, but can be grey, yellow, brown, red, blue or black, particularly when it forms marble. White streak, transparent to opaque, with a glassy, pearly or dull lustre. Fizzes with dilute hydrochloric acid. Crystals are variable in appearance, resembling the heads of nails, teeth, or distorted prisms. Much more common as granular or sugary aggregates. It makes up the bulk of limestones and marbles, and stalactites and stalagmites are usually composed of it. Forms the skeletons of most marine organisms, whether living or fossilized.

Witherite
BaCO₃
H. 3–3.5: S.G. 4.3
Orthorhombic.
Hydrothermal veins
Colourless, white or
grey, sometimes tinged
green, brown or yellow.
White streak. Glassy or
resinous lustre, transparent
to opaque. Unusually heavy
for a white mineral. Fizzes in
dilute hydrochloric acid.
Crystals always twinned into
pairs of pyramids with a
six-sided base. Also massive,
fibrous or granular. An ore of
barium, used in the manufacture
of specialist glass.

Siderite
FeCO₃
H. 3.5–4.5: S.G. 3.9
Trigonal. Widespread
occurrence
Typically brown, but also
yellow, grey, green, red or black.
Translucent with a white streak.
Crystals are usually rhombs or
saddle-shaped aggregates. Also
massive, granular, botryoidal.
An important ore of iron.

Aragonite
CaCO₃
H. 3.5–4: S.G. 2.9
Orthorhombic.
Sedimentary and
metamorphic rocks
Usually colourless
or white, but can
be yellow, red, green,
blue, purple or brown.
White streak. Glassy
or resinous lustre.
Fizzes with dilute
hydrochloric
acid. Crystals usually chisel-
shaped or needle-like. Found
in large crystalline masses, or
as columns or aggregates. Used
by many marine organisms for
building their skeletons, it is
common in fossils, but usually
changes to calcite within about
200 million years of the
organism's death.

Rhodochrosite

MnCO₃
H. 3.5–4.5: S.G. 3.4–3.6
Trigonal. Hydrothermal veins
Pink, purple or red. Pale pink
streak. Glassy or pearly lustre,
translucent to transparent.
Usually massive, granular or
banded. Crystals rhomb-shaped,
with one perfect cleavage.
Fragile and brittle. An
ornamental stone and ore of
manganese.

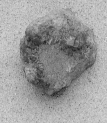

Smithsonite

ZnCO₃
H. 5: S.G. 4.4
Hexagonal. Hydrothermal veins
and limestones
White, yellow, brown, green,
blue, pink or purple. Streak white.
Translucent with a greasy or
glassy lustre. Usually botryoidal
or kidney-like masses, also
stalactitic, concretionary and
earthy. Crystals rare, usually
rounded rhombs with one
perfect cleavage. Brittle.

Hydrozincite

Zn₅(CO₃)₂(OH)₆
H. 2–2.5: S.G. 3.2–3.8
Monoclinic. Hydrothermal veins
and pegmatites
White or grey, with shades of
purple, brown and pink. White
streak. Translucent, with a dull
or silky lustre. Crystals never
exceed 1mm in length. Usually
found massive, as dense masses
or crusts which can be kidney
shaped. Very brittle.

Azurite

Cu₃(CO₃)₂(OH)₂
H. 3.5–4: S.G. 3.8
Monoclinic. Hydrothermal
veins and limestones
A distinctive rich azure-blue
colour. Pale blue streak.
Transparent to opaque, glassy to
dull. Crystals prismatic and
usually intergrown or in
radiating aggregates, and often
striated. Most commonly
massive, earthy or granular. Also
common in thin crusts, which
may be botryoidal.

Artinite

$Mg_2CO_3(OH)_2, 3H_2O$
H. 2-2.5; S.G. 2.0
Monoclinic. Hydrothermal veins
White or transparent with a
white streak. Always found as
silky balls of fibres or needle-like
crystals. Rarely found in small
veins. Fizzes in dilute
hydrochloric acid.

Magnesite

$MgCO_3$
H. 3.5–4.5; S.G. 3.0
*Trigonal. Widespread
occurrence*
Colourless, white, grey, yellow
or brown. Streak white. Glassy
or silky lustre, translucent to
transparent. Crystals rare,
usually rhombs with one perfect
cleavage. Frequently massive,
granular or compact, sometimes
fibrous and porcelain-like.
Curved fracture when broken.

Cerussite

$PbCO_3$
H. 3–3.5; S.G. 6.6
*Orthorhombic. Hydrothermal
veins*
Colourless, white or grey,
sometimes with impurities that
make it blue, green or black.
Transparent to translucent, with
a white streak and a greasy or
glassy lustre. Crystals elongated
and often striated, sometimes in
aggregates. Also massive.

Strontianite

$SrCO_3$
H. 3.5–4; S.G. 3.7
*Orthorhombic. Hydrothermal
veins and limestones*
Normally colourless or white,
sometimes pink, green or grey.
White streak. Translucent to
transparent, glassy lustre.
Dissolves and fizzes in dilute
hydrochloric acid. Usually
fibrous, or found as long,
needle-like crystals with one
perfect and two poor cleavages.
Also occurs massive, granular or
concretionary.

Tungstates, molybdates and chromates

The members of this small group are rarely encountered in the field, since environments where tungsten, molybdenum or chromium occur in sufficient quantities for minerals to form are few and far between. Hydrothermal veins are the most common sites of formation, and where they do occur, these minerals are often valuable ores, and are worked economically. They are generally soft, heavy and highly coloured: these distinctive characteristics make identification relatively easy.

Wulfenite
PbMoO$_4$
H. 2.8–3: S.G.6.5–7
Tetragonal. Hydrothermal veins
Colour variable, most frequently yellow or orange-red as seen here. Can also be brown, grey or even whitish. Streak white. Lustre is greasy or resinous. Translucent or transparent. Fracture is uneven and slightly conchoidal. Crystals are usually tabular and often thin, but prisms or cubes are sometimes found. Twinning is frequent. Most commonly found as fine- to coarse-grained granular masses. Wulfenite is a secondary mineral found in the zone of alteration of lead-rich hydrothermal deposits. It is much sought after by mineral collectors, and is an ore of molybdenum when found in quantity. Commonly found in association with barite, molybdenite and sphalerite.

Crocoite
PbCrO$_4$
H. 2.5–3: S.G. 6
Monoclinic. Hydrothermal veins
Bright orange-red, with an orange-yellow streak and very bright, glassy lustre. Translucent. Crystals are elongated prisms, often striated along their length. A rare secondary mineral, which is found where lead-rich hydrothermal veins are affected by oxygen.

Wolframite series
(Fe, Mn)WO₄
H. 4–4.5; S.G. 7.1–7.5
Monoclinic. Hydrothermal veins and pegmatites
This group of minerals forms a solid solution between iron tungstate and manganese tungstate. If only iron is present, the mineral is called ferberite; if only manganese, it is called heubnerite. Wolframite is the name given to intermediate compositions. The minerals of the series share many physical characteristics. Crystals are typically long prisms with striations on their sides. They

have one perfect cleavage parallel to the long axis. Twinning is common. They also all occur in granular or bladed masses.

Heubnerite is reddish-brown in colour, with a reddish-brown streak. It has a resinous lustre and is translucent to transparent. Ferberite is black, with a black streak. Slightly translucent to almost opaque, with a submetallic lustre. It is weakly magnetic due to its high iron content. Crystals tend to be elongated and markedly striated.

Wolframite (shown here) is intermediate in its physical properties between the two end members of the series. Its crystals are typically stubby prisms. Wolframite series minerals are often associated with quartz, feldspar, fluorite, hematite, cassiterite, arsenopyrite and topaz. All are ores of tungsten, which is widely used in the production of steel alloys.

Scheelite
CaWO₄
H. 4.5–5; S.G. 6.1
Tetragonal. Contact metamorphic rocks, hydrothermal veins and pegmatites
Colourless to white, green, grey, yellow or brown. Glassy lustre and white streak. Transparent to translucent. Tetragonal crystals, similar to quartz, with pyramidal cleavage. Most commonly found in contact

metamorphosed limestones, often in association with garnets, as well as in quartz veins and granitic pegmatites. An important ore of tungsten.

Stolzite
PbWO₄
H. 2.5–3; S.G. 7.9–8.3
Tetragonal. Hydrothermal veins
Green, red or brown with a colourless streak. Transparent to translucent with a resinous to greasy lustre. Pyramidal or tabular crystals, often with striated faces. Brittle, with an uneven or curved fracture.

Phosphates, arsenates and vanadates

These minerals are soft and have a low or moderate specific gravity. Many are highly coloured but have white or yellow streaks, making their identification fairly easy. The crystals of these minerals have an unusual structure, in that they incorporate large, electrically charged spaces in their frameworks. For this reason, they often "trap" scarce elements such as yttrium and uranium, and are used as sources of these precious substances.

Apatite

$Ca_5(PO_4)_3(F, Cl, OH)$
H. 5: S.G. 3.2
Hexagonal. Widespread occurrence

Very common. Variable in colour, usually green or brown, but can be colourless, blue, pink, purple, red, yellow or white. Streak always white, regardless of body colour. Dull, glassy lustre. Translucent to totally transparent. Crystals are usually prismatic with hexagonal bases, and are variable in length. Tabular crystals are also found. Cleavage is poor and in one direction only – across the length of the crystal. Commonly massive, when it can be granular, stalactitic or earthy. Brittle, with an uneven fracture.

Apatite occurs in igneous, metamorphic and sedimentary rocks, as well as hydrothermal veins. In marine sediments it is derived from vertebrate bones, and an impure form of apatite replaces limestones formed from the leaching of guano deposits. It is commonly associated with a wide variety of minerals, including albite, nepheline, muscovite and magnetite, and is of commercial value in the production of phosphate fertilizers.

Apatite is one of a group of minerals (known as the apatite group), which share are similar structure. Other members include pyromorphite, mimetite and vanadinite. Its name is derived from the Greek word for "deceit", as apatite is often mistaken for valuable gemstones such as aquamarine, beryl and tourmaline.

Pyromorphite
Pb₅(PO₄)₃Cl

$Pb_5(PO_4)_3Cl$
H. 3.5–4: S.G. 7.0

Hexagonal. Hydrothermal veins
Usually green, but also yellow,
orange, brown, grey, colourless
or white. Streak white.
Translucent with a greasy lustre.
Crystals are stubby hexagonal
prisms, often in groups and
parallel aggregates. Also found
as crusts and kidney shaped
masses. Brittle with an uneven
fracture. A member of the
apatite group.

Mimetite
$Pb_5(AsO_4)_3Cl$
H. 3.5–4: S.G. 7.3
Monoclinic. Hydrothermal veins
Orange-brown or yellow, rarely
colourless. Resinous lustre and
white streak. Transparent to
translucent. Occurs as rounded,
globular, barrel-like prisms
(sometimes known as
campyllite). Also found as
needle-like crystals and

botryoidal crusts. One of the
apatite group. Named after its
resemblance to pyromorphite
and vanadinite.

Torbernite
$Cu(UO_2)_2(PO_4)_2 . 8–12H_2O$
H. 2–2.5: S.G. 3.2
*Tetragonal. Hydrothermal veins
and pegmatites*
Shades of green with a similar
streak. Glassy lustre, transparent
to translucent. Thin, easily
separated flakes with perfect
cleavage. Radioactive. A
secondary mineral, formed with
autunite in weathered uranium-
bearing pegmatites and
hydrothermal veins that contain
uraninite.

Autunite
$Ca(UO_2)_2(PO_4)_2 . 10–12H_2O$
H. 2–2.5: S.G. 3.2
*Tetragonal. Hydrothermal veins
and pegmatites*
Bright yellow to greenish-yellow,
with a yellow streak and dull,
vitreous lustre. Translucent to
transparent, thin tabular
crystals. Micaceous aggregates
with perfect cleavage.

Variscite

(Al, Fe)PO₄. 2H₂O
H. 3.5–4.5: S.G. 2.2–2.9
Orthorhombic. Hydrothermal
veins
Various shades of green with a
white streak and an opaque,
waxy lustre. Transparent to
translucent. Crystals rare;
usually occurs in fine-grained
masses in veins and crusts that
form near the surface of
aluminium-rich rocks.

Wavellite

Al₃(OH)₃(PO₄)₂. 5H₂O
H. 3.5–4: S.G. 2.4
Orthorhombic. Hydrothermal
veins and metamorphic rocks
White, green, yellow, brown or
black. Glassy lustre, white
streak. Transparent or
translucent. Usually found as
radial, fibrous aggregates, in
globular or spherical nodules or
botryoidal crusts. Good cleavage
in three directions.

Annabergite

(Ni,Co)(AsO₄)₂. 8H₂O
H. 1.5: S.G. 3.1
Monoclinic. Hydrothermal veins
Pale green, with a pale green
streak. Translucent, with a dull,
glassy lustre. Most frequently
found as botryoidal crusts.
Crystals are rare and very small.
Annabergite is an alteration
product of nickel-cobalt
arsenides and sulphides. It has
no commercial value. Forms a
solid solution series with
erythrite.

Erythrite

Co₃(AsO₄)₂. 8H₂O
H. 1.5: S.G. 3.1
Monoclinic. Hydrothermal veins
Pink to purple, with a streak of
the same colour. Transparent to
opaque, with a glassy or earthy
lustre. Crystals are small,
sometimes occurring in radiating
bundles of needles or thin
prisms. Earthy crusts are more
common. An alteration product
of cobalt arsenides and
sulphides. Forms a solid solution
series with annabergite.

Descloizite-mottramite series

(Cu,Zn)PbVO₄OH
H. 3–3.5: S.G. 5.9 (mottramite)
6.2 (descloizite)
Orthorhombic. Hydrothermal veins

This is a two-member solid solution series. Descloizite (shown here) is zinc-rich with little copper; mottramite is copper-rich with little zinc. Reddish-brown to black (descloizite) with a yellow-orange-brown streak, or greenish-brown (mottramite) with a green streak. Both are transparent to opaque and most commonly occur as thin, micro-crystalline crusts. Crystals rare, small, usually pyramidal or prismatic, with uneven faces.

Carnotite

K₂(UO₂)₂(VO₄)₂. 1–3H₂O
H. 1–2: S.G. 4–5
Monoclinic. Sedimentary rocks

Yellow to greenish-yellow. Earthy lustre, yellow streak, strongly radioactive. Often found disseminated in sandstones or localized near petrified plant remains. An ore of both uranium and vanadium.

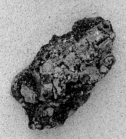

Olivenite

Cu₂AsO₄OH
H. 3: S.G. 4.4
Orthorhombic. Hydrothermal veins

Olive-green in colour, shading to brown or yellow. Yellow streak. Dull glassy or waxy lustre. Transparent or translucent to opaque. Found as needle-like crystals, as well as in fibrous, granular and earthy forms.

Vanadinite

Pb₅(VO₄)₃Cl
H. 2.7–3; S.G. 6.9
Hexagonal. Hydrothermal veins
Red, orange, brown or yellow.
White to pale yellow streak.
Resinous lustre. Transparent or
translucent. Occurs as small
prismatic crystals, as well as
needle-like and globular masses.
A rare mineral produced in
hydrothermal veins where lead-
rich minerals encounter air and
become oxidized. A member of
the apatite group. An ore of
vanadium, which is used in
alloys, dyes and as a catalyst.

Turquoise

CuAl₆(PO₄)₄(OH)₈·4H₂O
H. 5–6; S.G. 2.6–2.9
Triclinic. Hydrothermal veins
Distinctive bluish-green colour.
White to pale green streak.
Generally opaque, with a dull,
vitreous lustre. Crystals are rare.
It is usually found as a weakly
crystalline mass in reniform and
stalactitic forms as well as thin
veins. Formed as a secondary
mineral in the alteration zone of
aluminium-rich hydrothermal
replacement deposits in arid
regions. A gemstone.

Monazite

(Ce, La, Y, Th)PO₄
H. 5–5.5; S.G. 4.6–5.5
Monoclinic. Igneous rocks,
pegmatites and placers
Brown to yellow or reddish-
brown. Waxy or dull glassy
lustre. White streak, transparent
to translucent. Equal-sided
flattened or elongated crystals
are rare. More usually found as
small grains. An accessory
mineral in granites and
pegmatites. Highly resistant to
weathering, sometimes found in
beach or stream placer deposits.
Thorium-bearing monazite from
placer deposits is a significant
source of thorium oxide.

Amblygonite

(Li, Na)Al(PO₄)(F, OH)
H. 5.5–6: S.G. 3.1
Triclinic. Pegmatites

Usually white (as shown here), but can be tinted blue, green, grey, pink or yellow. Streak is always white. Varies from transparent through translucent to opaque and has a glassy or earthy lustre. Crystals are prismatic or lath-like. There is perfect cleavage in one direction and good cleavage in three others. Massive deposits also occur, with cleavage still present. Brittle, with a slightly curved fracture. It occurs almost exclusively in granite pegmatites, but is occasionally found in tin veins. Often occurs in association with tourmaline, lepidolite and spodumene, and may be confused with orthoclase. It is a useful source of lithium and a minor gemstone.

Adamite

Zn₂(AsO₄)(OH)
H. 3.5: S.G. 4.4
Orthorhombic. Hydrothermal veins

Usually light to browny-yellow, but may be pale green or even colourless. Streak is white or rarely slightly greenish. Transparent to translucent, with a bright glassy lustre. Crystals are small, elongated prisms, with cleavage in two directions, one good and one poor. Fracture is uneven. Commonly found coating small cavities (as shown here). It can also occur in ball-like or kidney-shaped aggregates. Found where hydrothermal veins are weathered in air, and is often associated with calcite and siderite.

Sulphates

The sulphate minerals are all soft, and some are soluble in water. Many have a white streak, even when the mineral has a strong body colour. This is because their body colour is produced by traces of impurities or by tiny defects in the mineral's structure, neither of which will leave a detectable streak on a streak plate.

Sulphates are usually sedimentary in origin and are often valuable sources of non-metallic elements, such as strontium. Some are commercially valuable in their own right, for instance gypsum is used extensively in building and medicine.

A

Barite

BaSO$_4$
H. 3–3.5; S.G. 4.5
Orthorhombic. Widespread occurrence

Usually colourless, white or grey, but can be tinted blue, brown, red or yellow by impurities. Streak is always white and the lustre is glassy. Transparent, translucent and opaque forms occur. Crystals are tabular (as shown in both specimens here) or prismatic, and often form diverging sheaves (A). Rosettes of platy crystals are common in arid areas, and are known as desert roses. There are three cleavages, one of which is perfect. Massive forms, often granular or fibous, are common. Fracture is uneven. It is noticeably heavy for a light-coloured, non-metallic mineral – a useful diagnostic character. It is named from the Greek word "barys" meaning heavy, in reference to its unexpected weight.

Barite is the most common barium mineral and is found in a wide variety of environments. It is frequently found in low-temperature hydrothermal veins, and in rock cavities in basalt and limestone. It also occurs in association with sedimentary iron and manganese deposits, or hot spring deposits. It is often associated with calcite and quartz, and with other sulphate minerals, such as gypsum and anhydrite. Barite has a variety of uses: as a filler in the manufacture of paints and paper; in the glass industry; and as a constituent of the heavy mud used in oil well-drilling operations.

Chalcanthite
CuSO₄. 5H₂O
H. 2.5; S.G. 2.3
Triclinic. Hydrothermal veins
Blue to green, with a white
streak. Glassy lustre, transparent
to translucent. Occurs as short
prismatic, or rarely tabular,
crystals. Can also be present as
stalactitic or botryoidal masses.
An alteration product of copper
minerals which readily dissolves
in water. Found only in desert
regions or as stalactitic growths
in copper mines or limestone
caverns.

Anhydrite
CaSO₄
H. 3–3.5; S.G. 3
*Orthorhombic. Evaporitic
environments*
White or grey, with tints of blue
or red. Streak white. Translucent
to transparent. Crystals are rare,
and it is usually found in
granular or fibrous masses.
Brittle, with three good
cleavages, which are at right
angles to each other and produce
rectangular cleavage fragments.
Anhydrite is an important rock-
forming mineral in evaporitic
environments on the Earth's
surface. It is often found in
association with calcite, gypsum,
dolomite and halite.

Anglesite
PbSO₄
H. 2.5–3; S.G. 6.4
*Orthorhombic. Hydrothermal
veins*
White or grey, may be tinted
yellow or green. Streak grey-
white. Resinous crystals, dull
when fine-grained. Transparent
to opaque. Tabular crystals
often found in association with
cerussite. Also occurs as
granular, stalactitic or nodular
masses. It is brittle with a curved
fracture, and feels
uncharacteristically heavy for a
white mineral, a reflection of its
high lead content.

A

B

Gypsum
CaSO₄. 2H₂O
H. 1.5–2: S.G. 2.3
Monoclinic. Widespread occurrence
Colourless, white, grey, brown, red or yellow. Glassy lustre, white streak. Single tabular crystals are usually elongated; contact-twinned crystals have a characteristic "fish-tail" appearance (A). In its fibrous form it is often called satin spar (B); in its transparent form, selenite; when it occurs in fine-grained white masses, it is known as alabaster. Some crystals and masses occur in a curved form; crystals may also be found in radial patterns. Cleavage in three directions, one good.

This common sulphate is found in several rock types. It is most commonly deposited as a salt water evaporite but is also found in volcanically-active regions and in hydrothermal replacement deposits. Readily alters to and from anhydrite. Used extensively in the building trade as plaster, in medicine as a cast for broken bones (plaster of Paris), as a fertilizer, and as a flux in the manufacture of glass. Alabaster may be carved.

Websterite
Al₂O₃
H. 1–2: S.G. 1.7
Monoclinic. Sediments formed by the weathering action of groundwater
An uncommon mineral. White, with a white streak, it is opaque and has a dull lustre. Most frequently occurs in kidney-shaped masses. It is peculiar in that it adheres to the tongue.

Alunite

$KAl_3(SO_4)_2(OH)_6$
H. 3,5-4: S.G. 2.7
Trigonal. Volcanic rocks
White, yellow, grey or red.
Streak white. Glassy lustre,
transparent or translucent.
Rarely occurs as small, white
crystals. Usually forms as
granular masses in zones of
volcanic activity, when sodium-
and potassium-rich feldspars are
altered by water containing
sulphuric acid. Poor cleavage.
Used in the production of alum.

Linarite

$PbCu(SO_4)(OH)_2$
H. 2.5: S.G. 5.3
Monoclinic. Hydrothermal veins
Blue colour and streak.
Translucent with a glassy lustre.
Prismatic or tabular crystals
have good cleavage in one
direction and poor in a second.
Frequently forms crusts. A
secondary mineral found in the
weathered alteration zone of
hydrothermal replacement
deposits, and often associated
with copper, lead or silver veins.
Similar in colour to azurite but
softer and heavier.

Celestite

$SrSO_4$
H. 3–3.5: S.G. 4.0
*Orthorhombic. Evaporitic
environments*
Colourless or white, with pale
"celestial" blue tints common.
Also found with yellow, brown
or red tints. Streak white.
Glassy lustre, translucent to
transparent. Occurs in tabular
crystals that resemble those of
barite; celestite may be
distinguished by its lower
density. Also found in fibrous,
cleavable masses. Good cleavage
in at least one direction. A
source of strontium, which is
used in sugar refining.

Blödite

$MgSO_4$
H. 2.5; S.G. 2.2
Monoclinic. Evaporitic
environments
A rare mineral. Generally colourless, but can be greenish, yellowish or shades of red. Streak white. Translucent or transparent. Glassy lustre. Crystals are usually short and prismatic. Also occurs as granulous or fibrous masses. No cleavage. Has a weak salty taste.

Jarosite

$KFe_3(SO_4)_2(OH)$
H. 2.5-3.5; S.G. 2.9-3.2
Trigonal. Hydrothermal veins
Yellow or brown with a yellow streak. Translucent, with a glassy, resinous or earthy lustre. Sometimes forms small, indistinct, tabular crystals, but is usually found as an earthy crust.

Langite

$CuSO_4$. $3Cu(OH)_2$. H_2O
H. 2.5-3; S.G. 3.5
Orthorhombic. Hydrothermal
veins
Very uncommon. A distinctive sky-blue or greenish-blue mineral. Streak white. Crystals are rare and glassy. More common as crusts.

Thenhardite

Na_2SO_4
H. 2.5-3; S.G. 2.7
Orthorhombic. Evaporitic
environments
White, yellow or brown. Streak white. Glassy lustre, translucent to transparent. Soluble in water with a weak, salty taste. Crystals are tabular and usually cross-twinned, but it is more commonly found as a granular mass with other evaporites. Good basal cleavage, and an uneven fracture. It may rarely occur near volcanic fumaroles (those vents that expel steam and other gases, but do not erupt lava).

Borates

Most of the borate minerals are soft and dissolve in water. They are usually white or colourless, with a white streak, translucent to transparent and have a low specific gravity. They are the main sources of boron, which is used in the manufacture of specialist glass, glass fibre and ceramic glaze. Boron is also used as a bleaching agent in detergents.

Ulexite
$NaCaB_5O_9. 8H_2O$
H. 2.5; S.G. 2.0
Triclinic. Evaporitic environments
Crystals are colourless and glassy, masses are white and silky. White streak. Transparent to translucent. Usually found in spongy masses of hair-like fibres called cotton balls. Crystals are rare, long needles. Dissolves in hot water.

Meyerhofferite
$2CaO. 3B_2O_3. 7H_2O$
H. 2; S.G. 2.1
Triclinic. Evaporitic environments
Very uncommon. Colourless to white, with a white streak. Crystals are prismatic or tabular. There is one good cleavage. A massive, fibrous form is also known.

Colemanite
$Ca_2B_6O_{11}. 5H_2O$
H. 4–4.5; S.G. 2.4
Monoclinic. Evaporitic environments
White, colourless or grey, with a white streak. Transparent to translucent, with a glassy lustre. Crystals usually prisms with one good and one poor cleavage. Also found massive

Borax
$Na_2B_4O_7. 10H_2O$
H. 2–2.5; S.G. 1.7
Monoclinic. Evaporitic environments
Colourless or white, sometimes with traces of grey, yellow, or blue. White streak. Transparent to opaque, glassy or earthy lustre. Sweet taste. Crystals are stubby prisms that decompose in air. Crusts and earthy masses are more common.

Silicates

Over 80% of the minerals on the surface of the Earth are silicates. This very diverse group accounts for about half of all known mineral types, including all the dominant rock-forming minerals. All igneous and metamorphic rocks are made almost exclusively of silicate minerals, as are all of the clastic sediments. Though it is difficult to generalize about so large a group, the silicates do have certain physical characteristics in common: most have a white streak regardless of body colour, and most have a low to moderate specific gravity. All the silicates are made up of the same chemical building blocks – groups of one silicon atom surrounded by four atoms of oxygen. These fundamental subunits can join together, or be separated by other elements. Silicates are conventionally classified according to the type of links that form between these silica groups. The six major categories – island, couplet, ring, chain, framework and layer silicates are considered below.

Island silicates

These are silicates whose silica groups are completely seperated from one another by atoms of other elements.

Andalusite

Al_2SiO_5
H. 6.5–7.5: S.G. 3.1
Orthorhombic. Metamorphic rocks
White, grey, pink, red, green or yellow. White streak. Dull glassy lustre, transparent to translucent. Crystals are prisms, nearly square in cross section, with two good cleavage planes. One variety, chiastolite (A), shows a diagonal cross pattern on its cross-section. A minor gemstone.

A

Kyanite

Al_2SiO_5
H. 5 parallel to crystal length, 7 across the length: S.G. 3.6
Triclinic. Metamorphic rocks
Patchy colour, with blues and greens predominating. Sometimes grey-white or black. Streak white. Glassy lustre, transparent to translucent. Found as long, bladed crystals with good lengthwise cleavage. The unusual hardness is distinctive. A minor gemstone, which is often found in schists and gneisses.

Sillimanite

Al₂SiO₅
H. 6.5–7.5: S.G. 3.2
Orthorhombic. Metamorphic rocks
White, sometimes with a grey, blue or yellow tint. Streak white. Glassy lustre, transparent to translucent. Slender, prismatic crystals, usually found in fibrous or columnar masses, have good lengthwise cleavage. Found in schists and gneisses.

Titanite

CaTiSiO₅
H.5–5.5: S.G. 3.5
Monoclinic. Igneous and metamorphic rocks
Also known as sphene. Yellow-green or brown to black in colour, with a greasy lustre and white streak. Transparent to translucent. Crystals are sharp-edged and wedge-shaped. There are two distinct cleavages parallel to the crystal faces. Brittle, with a curved fracture. An accessory mineral of granitic, plutonic rocks, also found in schists and gneisses. A unusual gemstone.

Olivine series

(Mg, Fe)₂SiO₄
H. 6.5–7: S.G. 3.2–4.3
Orthorhombic. Igneous rocks
Olive-green in colour, shading to yellow or brown. White streak, glassy lustre. Found as transparent (variety peridot, which is a gemstone) to translucent embedded grains (specimen A shows them embedded in basalt). Crystals are rare, with two poor cleavages. It is an essential component of all silica-poor rocks. Dunite is a rock composed entirely of olivine; it is shown here as specimen B. Olivine is part of a solid solution series, the end members of which are fayalite (Fe₂SiO₄) and forsterite (Mg₂SiO₄). It alters readily to complex clay minerals and talc.

Garnet group

Mainly aluminium silicates
H. 6.5–7.5; S.G. 3.6–4.3
Cubic. Metamorphic and
occasionally igneous rocks

A closely related group of common minerals. The main types – grossular, almandine, andradite, uvarovite and spessartine – are described on this and the following page. All belong to the cubic system and occur in many colours with various sizes of crystals. All have a white streak, and generally have a glassy lustre.

Transparent, translucent or opaque. Crystals are commonly dodecahedrons or trapezohedrons. No garnet possesses cleavage, although partings do occur. All are brittle, with an uneven fracture and are used as industrial abrasives. Several are of gemstone quality.

Garnets are usually found in metamorphic rocks, often in great abundance; indeed they characterize certain types of schist.

Grossular
$Ca_2Al_2(SiO_4)_3$
Yellow, green, white, pink or brown. The commonest of the garnets, usually found in metamorphosed limestones.

Almandine
$Fe_3Al_2(SiO_4)_3$
A purple, red or brown gemstone usually found in schists and gneisses.

Andradite
Ca₃Fe(SiO₄)₃

$Ca_3Fe(SiO_4)_3$

Usually brown in colour and found in contact-metamorphosed limestones. Green colour (variety demantoid) and yellow colour (variety topazolite) are found in altered gabbros and peridotites. Black colour (variety melanite) found in lavas and silica-poor plutons.

Uvarovite
$Ca_3Cr_2(SiO_4)_3$

Emerald-green in colour. Found in chromium-rich peridotites and in unusual metamorphic rocks that have been heated with abundant water. A rare variety of garnet.

Spessartine
$Mn_3Al_2(SiO_4)_3$

Usually rich shades of brown, but can be yellowish to reddish. Found in granitic pegmatites, which are the source of the specimen shown here, and in a high-pressure form of schist known as blueschist (so called because it contains blue glaucophane).

Topaz

$Al_2 (SiO_4) (OH,F)_2$
H. 8: S.G. 3.5
Orthorhombic. Igneous rocks and hydrothermal veins
Colourless, white, yellow, pink, and pale shades of blue or green. Glassy lustre. Too hard to produce a streak. Translucent to transparent, prismatic, vertically striated crystals with perfect, basal cleavage. The fracture is uneven but slightly curved. Found in granitic pegmatites, high-temperature hydrothermal veins and replacement deposits, and rarely in cavities in rhyolite. A gemstone that is sometimes mistaken for quartz, but is harder and has cleavage.

Staurolite

$Fe_2Al_9Si_4O_{22} (OH)_2$
H. 7–7.5: S.G. 3.8
Monoclinic. Metamorphic rocks
Usually brown in colour, but can be darker shades of yellow or reddish-brown. White streak, dull glassy lustre. Translucent to opaque crystals may be single, elongated and tabular (when it is a minor gemstone), or more distinctively, twinned, when they form a right-angled "cross", which usually has a rough surface. There is one poor cleavage. Fracture is uneven or slightly curved. Found in mica schists and gneisses.

Zircon

$ZrSiO_4$
H. 7.5: S.G. 4.7
Tetragonal. Igneous rocks and placers
Usually brown, but turns blue with heat treatment. Colourless, yellow, red, green and orange forms also occur. Too hard to give a streak. Glassy lustre. Transparent to translucent. Crystals have a square cross section and terminate in prisms. It has two poor cleavages, and is brittle with an uneven fracture. An accessory mineral in igneous rocks. It is highly resistant to weathering and is found in beach and stream placer deposits. A gemstone. Sometimes mistaken for vesuvianite, but is much heavier.

Couplet silicates

These minerals contain pairs of silica groups, separated by other elements. Unusually for the silicates, this group includes no significant rock-forming minerals. Most couplet silicates are found in metamorphic rocks.

Epidote Series

A solid solution series of complex calcium, aluminium and iron silicates
H. 6–6.5; S.G. 3.2–4
Monoclinic. Metamorphic rocks
Two members of the series – piedmontite and epidote – are described here. Colours vary but all have a glassy lustre and the streak is often grey-white. Crystals are frequently striated. They are usually long, slender prisms, terminating in two sloping faces. Shorter, equant prisms also occur. Crystals have one perfect cleavage. Usually formed from the metamorphism of calcium-rich sedimentary and igneous rocks, but may also be found in pegmatites and in cavities in basalt lavas.

Piedmontite

$Ca_2(Al,Fe,Mn)_3(SiO_4)_3(OH)$
Red, purple or black, with an unusual red streak. Transparent to nearly opaque. Normally found as poor rod-shaped crystals or as granular aggregates.

Epidote

$Ca_2(Al,Fe)_3(SiO_4)_3(OH)$
Green colour predominates, shading to yellow, brown or black. Transparent to nearly opaque. Granular masses or radiating fibrous groups (as shown here) are characteristic. A minor gemstone.

Zoisite

$Ca_2Al_3(SiO_4)_3(OH)$
H. 6; S.G. 3.2–3.4
Orthorhombic. Metamorphic rocks
Grey, greenish or yellowish-brown, sometimes pink (variety thulite), or blue (variety tanzanite). White streak. Glassy lustre, pearly on the cleavage face. Its translucent, long prismatic crystals are striated along their length. Sometimes considered to be part of the epidote series. Found in calcium-rich metamorphic rocks.

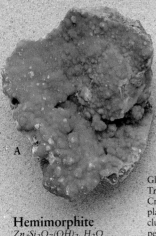

A

Hemimorphite

$Zn_4Si_2O_7(OH)_2 \cdot H_2O$
H. 4.5–5: S.G. 3.4
Orthorhombic. Hydrothermal veins

Usually white, but can also be blue or brown (as shown here), green, or yellow. The colour is produced by trace impurities of copper and iron. Streak white, regardless of body colour.

Glassy, greasy or dull lustre. Transparent to translucent. Crystals are usually small, thin plates that often form radiating clusters or coxcombs. One perfect cleavage. The mineral is brittle with an uneven or slightly curved fracture. Earthy or botryoidal (specimen A) masses are common. Hemimorphite is a secondary mineral formed when zinc-bearing hydrothermal veins are exposed to weathering.

Often found in association with gypsum and calcite.

Vesuvianite

$Ca_{10}Mg_2Al_4(SiO_4)_5(Si_2O_7)_2(OH)_4$
H. 6.5: S.G. 3.4
Tetragonal. Metamorphic rocks

Also known as idocrase. Most often brown or green as shown here, but can also be yellow or blue. Streak always white. Lustre is usually resinous or glassy. Transparent to translucent. Crystals are short, sometimes elongated, prisms with a square cross-section and one poor cleavage. Brittle, with an uneven fracture. In its crystalline form, vesuvianite is sometimes mistaken for zircon, though the latter is harder and heavier. The mineral is also found in striated columnar and earthy masses.

The massive form is usually known as californite: it is colourless, with a green streak. Californite resembles jade in some respects, but is harder.

Found in contact-metamorphosed limestones, but also known from volcanic rocks. A minor gemstone.

Ring silicates

Rings of three, four or six sets of silica groups make up the framework of these minerals. The ring silicates have complex formulas and contain a wide variety of elements. They are widespread, especially in metamorphic situations. In general, they are not important rock-forming minerals, though cordierite can be present in significant quantities in some contact metamorphic rocks. Ring silicates are fairly hard, scoring between 5 and 8 on Mohs' scale, and most have valuable gem varieties.

Tourmaline group

(Na,Ca)(Mg,Fe^{2+}, Fe^{3+}, Al, Mn, Li)$_3$Al$_6$(BO$_3$)$_3$(Si$_6$O$_{18}$)(OH,F)$_4$
H. 7: S.G. 3–3.3
Trigonal. Widespread occurrence

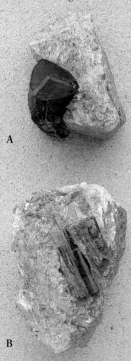

A

This group includes buergerite, dravite, elbaite and schorl. Two varieties are shown here – schorl (A) and elbaite (variety rubellite) (B). Members of the group can be black, white, blue, green, red, pink, brown or colourless. One crystal can grade from green at one end to pink at the other, through colourless in the middle. Some varieties change colour from natural to artificial light. Streak white, regardless of body colour. Translucent to transparent, with a glassy lustre. Crystals are long (up to 1 m) and prismatic, with pronounced vertical striations. The cross section is triangular, with each side slightly convex. Cleavage poor. Brittle with a curved fracture. Many colours are valuable as gems. The tourmalines are most common in hydrothermal veins, and some igneous and metamorphic rocks.

B

Axinite

(Ca, Mn, Fe)$_3$Al$_2$B(SiO$_4$)$_4$
H. 6.5–7: S.G. 3.4
Triclinic. Metamorphic rocks
Violet-brown, grey, black, colourless, pale violet or pale red. Transparent to translucent with a white streak. Glassy lustre. Crystals are flattened wedges, often occurring as bladed aggregates; they are sometimes striated. Also found as lamellar or granular masses. One moderately good cleavage. Brittle with a curved fracture.

Beryl

$Be_3Al_2Si_6O_{18}$
H. 7.5–8: S.G. 2.6–2.9
Hexagonal. Granites and pegmatites
Colourless, white, green, blue, yellow, pink, orange, red and all shades in between. Common varieties are often rather milky in appearance. Streak white. Translucent to transparent, with a glassy lustre. Found as six-sided prismatic crystals, which are often etched and striated. Crystals have been known to reach lengths of 9 m. Also massive and columnar. Several colours of beryl are valuable as gemstones, especially when transparent. The main ore of beryllium.

Cordierite

$(Mg, Fe^{3+})_2Al_4Si_5O_{18}$
H. 7–7.5: S.G. 2.6
Orthorhombic. Widespread occurrence
Usually blue or violet, rarely grey or brown. Too hard to have a streak. Transparent to translucent, with a glassy lustre. Crystals are stubby prisms, which are violet or blue when looked at from the base and colourless when viewed from the side. This is an important diagnostic property.

Dioptase

$CuSiO_2(OH)_2$
H. 5: S.G. 3.3
Trigonal. Hydrothermal veins
Emerald to bluish-green in colour. Streak pale greenish-blue. Glassy lustre, which is greasy on fractured or cleaved surfaces. Crystals prismatic, terminating in rhombs. Three perfect cleavages. The mineral is brittle and fractures leaving an uneven or curved surface. Also found massive and as crystal aggregates. Minor use as jewellery – popular with collectors.

Chain silicates

Single or double chains of silica groups run through these minerals. The chain silicates include two of the most important rock-forming mineral groups – the amphiboles and pyroxenes. Pyroxenes are an essential component of most silica-poor igneous rocks, whilst amphiboles, such as actinolite, make up many metamorphic rocks.

Rhodonite

MnSiO₃
H. 5.5–6: S.G. 3.7
Triclinic. Metamorphic and igneous rocks
Pink or red to brownish-red; more rarely grey, green or yellow. Often veined by black manganese oxide. White streak. Glassy lustre, transparent to translucent. Crystals are uncommon and usually tabular with rough surfaces. Usually found in cleavable masses, which can be used as an ornamental stone when polished. Cleavage is good in two directions. Fracture is uneven or curved. Often associated with garnet and calcite. A minor gemstone.

Wollastonite

CaSiO₃
H. 4.5–5: S.G. 2.9
Triclinic. Metamorphic rocks
Usually colourless, white or grey, but can be tinted yellow, pink, red or brown. Streak white, regardless of body colour. Transparent to translucent. Crystals are rare, needle like, and have a glassy lustre. Fibrous masses with a silky lustre are much more common. Cleavable masses also occur. Cleavage is good in two directions, which are almost at right angles to each other. Brittle, with a splintery, uneven fracture. Soluble in dilute hydrochloric acid. Found in metamorphosed limestones through which silica-rich fluids have passed. Often associated

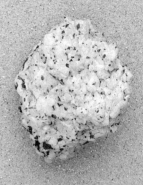

with calcite and grossular garnets. Wollastonite is mined where abundant; it is used in the ceramics industry and as a filler in paints.

Amphibole group

All have (Si, Al)O$_4$ groups linked into single chains
H. 5–6: S.G. 2.9–3.5
Monoclinic. Igneous and metamorphic rocks

A large group of minerals, often difficult to distinguish from each other in the field. Six members of the group are described on this and the following page – hornblende, crocidolite, glaucophane, actinolite, nephrite and tremolite; the last three are members of the actinolite-tremolite solid solution series. All occur as fibrous or prismatic crystals, the prisms being elongated and six-sided with diamond-shaped cross sections. Amphiboles resemble members of the pyroxene group, but may be distinguished by close examination of their crystals, which have two cleavage planes separated from one another by 56°. All are transparent to translucent and have a glassy lustre and a white streak unless otherwise indicated.

Hornblende

NaCa$_2$(Mg,Fe,Al)$_5$(Si,Al)$_8$O$_{22}$(OH)$_2$

Black or dark greenish-black. Crystals are prismatic, with a diamond-shaped cross section. Granular, radiating and columnar masses also occur.

Riebeckite

Na$_2$Fe$_3{}^{2+}$Fe$_2{}^{3+}$Si$_8$O$_{22}$(OH)$_2$

Dark blue to black prisms. Translucent to opaque. The long, fibrous, flexible variety known as crocidolite is shown here; in this case it is replaced by silica to form tiger eye.

Glaucophane

Na$_2$(Mg,Fe)$_3$Al$_2$Si$_8$O$_{22}$(OH)$_2$

Blue to bluish-black with a grey-blue streak. Found almost exclusively in blueschists. Crystals are prismatic, with diamond-shaped cross sections.

Actinolite

$Ca_2(Mg,Fe)_5Si_8O_{22}(OH)_2$
The iron-rich end member of the actinolite-tremolite series. Green, greyish-green to black. Lustre varies from glassy through pearly to silky depending on the mineral habit. Crystals are commonly prismatic, but can also be needle-like or bladed. Common in schists and serpentine.

Nephrite

$Ca_2(Mg,Fe)_5Si_8O_{22}(OH)_2$
A tough, compact member of the actinolite-tremolite series. Colours range from all shades of green to white and shades of grey, brown and purple. Found in serpentine that has been metamorphosed. One of the true jade gemstones.

Tremolite *(not shown)*

$Ca_2Mg_5Si_8O_{22}(OH)_2$
The magnesium-rich end member of the tremolite-actinolite series. White to dark grey, yellow, green, pink or purple in colour. Fibrous, most often in radiating sheaves; the small fibres are flexible. Usually found in metamorphosed dolomites. Readily alters to talc. Used as asbestos.

Pyroxene group

*All have (Si, Al)O₄ groups
linked into single chains
H. 5–6: S.G. 3.2–3.9
Orthorhombic (enstatite-
hypersthene series) or
monoclinic (diopside-
hedenbergite-augite series).
Igneous and metamorphic rocks*

A large group of minerals, often
difficult to distinguish from each
other in the field. Described on
this and the following page are
hypersthene and enstatite, which
are members of the enstatite-
hypersthene solid solution series;
and five pyroxenes of the
diopside-hedenbergite-augite
solid solution series, namely
augite, spodumene, diopside,
aegrine and jadeite.

All are transparent to
translucent and have a glassy
lustre unless otherwise stated.
Streak variable, but normally
greyish-white. Crystals are all
short, four or six-sided prisms
with almost square shaped cross-
sections. They have two
distinctive cleavages separated
from one another by almost 90°,
which is the obvious way of
distinguishing pyroxenes from
the amphibole group, which they
otherwise resemble.

Hypersthene

(Mg, Fe)SiO₃

The magnesium-poor end
member of the enstatite-
hypersthene series (no pure
FeSiO₃ exists). Usually found in
blackish-brown shades.
Translucent (in thin slices) to
opaque. May have a bronze-like
lustre. Crystals rare, stubby and
prismatic. Normally found in
lamellar masses in silica-poor
igneous rocks. Breaks with an
uneven fracture.

Enstatite

MgSiO₃

The magnesium-rich end
member of the enstatite-
hypersthene series. It varies in
colour from grey to black, but
can also be greenish, yellowish
or a bronzy-brown. Most
specimens have a glassy or silky
lustre. However, the bronze
variety (known as bronzite) is
almost metallic. Crystals are rare
and usually occur in aggregates.
Enstatite is most often found in a
poorly-crystalline form,
disseminated through silica-poor
igneous rocks. Bronzite and
emerald green enstatite are used
as gemstones.

Augite
CaNa(Mg,Fe,Al)(Al,Si)$_2$O$_6$

The commonest pyroxene, found in various shades of black, dark brown and green with occasional shades of purple. Streak green. Glassy or submetallic lustre; brittle, with an uneven fracture. It is widespread in basalts, dolerites and gabbros, less so in metamorphic rocks. Found in association with feldspars and olivine.

Spodumene
LiAlSi$_2$O$_6$

White, grey, yellow, green, pink or purple with a white streak. Crystals are long, lath-like and flat with striations. Usually found in pegmatites, it is an ore of lithium. Some of its colour forms are used as gemstones.

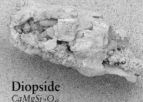

Diopside
CaMgSi$_2$O$_6$

Usually light green, but can also be black, brown or white-grey. Most often found in rod-like or fibrous aggregates. Common in calcium-rich metamorphic rocks and some silica-poor igneous rocks. The transparent type is a gemstone.

Aegerine
NaFe^{3+}Si$_2$O$_6$

Reddish-brown, dark green to black with a pale yellow-grey streak. It has long, vertically-striated crystals with blunt terminations and is commonly found in fibrous or needle-like aggregates. The variety acmite (shown here) has acute terminations to the crystals. Found in igneous rocks.

Jadeite
NaAlSi$_2$O$_6$

One of the two jade minerals. Ranges in colour from white to various shades of green. Glassy, dull or waxy lustre. Crystals are rare and blade-like; they are sometimes found in felt-like mats. The mineral is usually found massive. It is brittle, fracturing easily into splinters. Occurs in metamorphic rocks.

Framework silicates

These minerals are made up of a three-dimensional, interconnected network of silica groups. As a result they tend to lack good cleavage. Quartz, the extreme example, contains nothing but interconnected silica groups.

Quartz group

SiO₂
H. 7; S.G. 2.7
Trigonal. Widespread occurrence

The commonest mineral in the Earth's crust, making up about 12% by volume. Two distinct types of quartz are found: the coarse crystalline forms (which frequently contain impurities that alter the crystal's colour) are described on this and the following page; and the compact microcrystalline forms, which are collectively known as chalcedony. Coloured forms of chalcedony usually have individual names: they are described on pp. 104 and 105.

Quartz is colourless when pure (rock crystal), but is often coloured by impurities. Lighter-coloured forms are transparent, darker forms are translucent. Chalcedony is opaque. All types have a glassy lustre and white streak. Crystals are prismatic, commonly six-sided, often horizontally striated. Lacks cleavage. Formed in silica-rich igneous rocks and common in hydrothermal veins. Because it is highly resistant to weathering, quartz is also found in a wide variety of sediments, which may become consolidated into rock. It can even be derived from organic skeletal remains to form flint or chert. Although stable under metamorphic conditions it is easily mobilized and is therefore a constituent of many metamorphic rocks.

Commonly used as an abrasive, and in the manufacture of glass. Can be carved. Many forms are gemstones.

Rock crystal

A pure, colourless variety of quartz, often found in pegmatites and geodes. The specimen shown here is slightly smoky.

Milky quartz

White in colour due to minute liquid intrusions that scatter light. The commonest form in hydothermal veins.

Citrine

Yellow colour caused by ferric iron hydroxide impurities. Commonly found with amethyst.

Rose quartz
Pale pink to rose-red colour caused by manganese or titanium ions. Frequently found in pegmatites.

Tiger's eye
Yellow or yellow-brown colour that is chatoyant (reflecting a "wavy" band of light). Occurs rarely as blue "falcon's eye".

Amethyst
Purple colour caused by ferric iron impurities. Commonly found in cavities in volcanic rocks. Crystals often vary in colour along their length; their bases are frequently paler than their tips, and they sometimes include sets of light and dark bands. Alters to yellow citrine when heated.

Smoky quartz
Pale brown to blackish colour caused by irradiation; naturally-occurring radioactive isotopes damage the crystal lattice of otherwise colourless quartz. The defects produced in this way cause the mineral to absorb certain wavelengths of light, thus altering its colour. Becomes colourless when heated to 225°C. Found in pegmatites and hydrothermal veins.

Chalcedony
(Variety sard)
Yellow to reddish-brown colour
caused by the presence of iron
oxides. Shown here is an
unusual specimen in which
banded chalcedony has been
broken and then reset in a
matrix of colourless quartz.

Chalcedony
(Variety chrysoprase)
Apple-green colour caused by
the presence of hydrated nickel
silicate. It is rarely as clear as the
other varieties of chalcedony.

Chalcedony
(Variety aventurine)
This pinkish variety of
chalcedony contains abundant
white mica inclusions. This gives
it an unusual twinkling lustre
and an almost platy appearance.

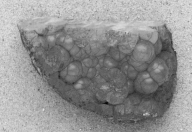

Chalcedony
(Variety carnelian)
Varies in colour from orange to
a deep blood-red. Colour is
often irregular, with darker
spots and streaks present.
Translucent to transparent in
thin slices. The massive,
botryoidal form shown here is
typical of the mineral's habit.

Agate

(Similar to moss agate and onyx). These banded forms of chalcedony are made up of successive layers of different colour. Agate is banded by "wavy" lines and patterns, onyx is parallel-banded and moss agate has "moss-like" dendritic inclusions. Agate is frequently dyed to improve its colour and increase its value. Brown and orange forms as shown here are natural; blue agate is artificially coloured.

Flint

Grey siliceous nodules found in chalk. The silica that makes up flint is derived from the skeletons of microscopic marine animals and plants. The skeletons dissolved after their death, and the silica was subsequently redeposited as flint. Fossils are often composed of flint.

Jasper

Strong shades of dark red, brown, yellow, green or black due to the presence of iron oxides, which can make up 20% of the mineral. Sometimes found as petrified wood.

Cristobalite

SiO₂
H. 6.5; S.G. 2.3
Tetragonal. Igneous rocks
White, grey, blue, yellow or brown. Streak white, regardless of body colour. Translucent to opaque, no cleavage. Crystals small (no more than about 4 mm long), octahedral and are usually found in cavities in igneous rocks. The specimen pictured here shows cristobalite growing in gas bubbles within odsidian. This quartz-rich igneous rock has a typical conchoidal fracture. Cristobalite has the same chemical composition as quartz but forms, and is stable, at much higher pressures and temperatures.

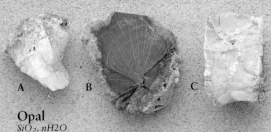

A   B   C

Opal

SiO₂. nH2O
H. 5.5–6; S.G. 2.1
Amorphous. Pegmatites
White, bluish white, shades of yellow, brown, green, grey or even black. Streak white. A form of hydrous silica, which is never found in crystal form. Occurs as veinlets, cavity fillings or concretionary crusts which may be botryoidal, reniform or stalactitic. No cleavage. Precious opal (C) shows a characteristic optical property known as opalescence. A play of colours – typically blue, green, purple and red – is seen in the mineral: this is caused by the scattering of reflected light by minute pore spaces between the spheres of silica that make up the mineral. The presence of the pore spaces makes opal fragile; minute fractures form easily, giving the mineral a "crazed" appearance.

Common opal (A) tends to be milky. It commonly replaces wood after it has been buried; the fine structure of wood may be preserved in this way (B). Normally precipitated from silica-rich solutions, opal can be found as petrified wood, or replacing the skeletons of marine organisms.

Feldspar group

A most important group of rock-forming minerals. All are complex aluminium silicates. Crystals have a glassy lustre, white streak, and two good cleavages at almost 90° to each other. Many are difficult to identify because they occur as small grains within the matrix of igneous rocks and do not show good crystal faces. The feldspars fall into two main groups – the potash and the plagioclase series, which are described below.

Potash feldspars

Monoclinic or triclinic. Igneous and metamorphic rocks
KAlSi$_3$O$_8$ (often with sodium replacing potassium)
H. 6: S.G. 2.6
Common constituents of many igneous rocks. Crystals are prismatic and twinning is common. The potash feldspars are described on this page.

Orthoclase

(Below)
Monoclinic. Usually white, grey, pink; rarely yellow. Common in silica-rich igneous rocks, metamorphic rocks and arkose sandstones.

Microcline

(Above)
Triclinic. Green, white or reddish brown, commonly found intergrown with quartz, especially in pegmatites.

Adularia

(Above)
Monoclinic. White, transparent or opalescent, often called moonstone. The beige-white angular crystals visible on the top right of this rock are typical.

107

Plagioclase feldspars

(Na,Ca)Al(Al,Si)Si$_2$O$_8$
H. 6: S.G. 2.6–2.8
Triclinic. Igneous and
metamorphic rocks
The most abundant of the rock-forming minerals. Plagioclase feldspars are necessary components of almost all igneous rocks. They are found throughout the Earth's crust and in the lavas of surface eruptions. They are common, almost ubiquitous, in metamorphic areas, and although they weather rapidly when exposed to the elements, they persist in some sediments, such as impure sandstones. These minerals break down to clays, which form the bulk of fine-grained sediments. Kaolinite is a weathering product of feldspar.

Colour ranges from white or grey, through shades of blue, green or red, to black. Streak white. Glassy lustre. Crystals rare, except for albite and oligoclase, which occur as small blades with multiple twinning. They occur more commonly as irregular grains.

The plagioclase feldspars form a solid solution series with albite as the pure sodium end member and anorthite the pure calcium end member. The rest of the series have varying proportions of both; they are defined by the percentage of albite that they contain.

The plagioclase feldspars are described on this and the following page.

Albite

(90–100% albite). Almost always white, with a white streak. Transparent to translucent. Crystal faces have a glassy lustre, while cleavage planes are pearly. Three cleavages occur, two of which are good and at right angles to each other. The mineral is brittle, with an uneven fracture.

Anorthite

(0-10% albite). The least-frequently found of the plagioclase feldspars, then usually in contact-metamorphosed limestones. Varies in colour from white to dark grey or black. Glassy lustre. Brittle, with an uneven fracture. Three cleavages.

Andesine

(50-70% albite). Common in fine-grained andesite lavas. Usually white or creamy-white, with a vitreous lustre. Opaque to translucent. Has three cleavages and a brittle, uneven fracture.

Labradorite

(30-50% albite). Usually green or blue. Often found in cleavable masses that display a dark blue to greenish-black iridescence. Cleavage surfaces have a pearly lustre, while crystal faces are vitreous. The cleavage planes can often be seen within the mineral. Commonly occurs in silica-poor igneous rocks, such as basalt and gabbro. May be classed as a gemstone. Slabs of large labradorite aggregates are commonly used for decorative facings.

Oligoclase

(70-90% albite). Most often white or beige in colour. Crystal faces have a glassy lustre, while cleavage surfaces are pearly. Has three cleavage planes. Sometimes occurs in closely-spaced multiple twins, but is more usually found massive in plutonic rocks. The light opalescent form is known as moonstone.

Feldspathoid group

A group of minerals with similar chemical composition to the feldspars, but with less silica in their structure. They usually crystallize instead of the feldspar minerals in silica-poor magmas and are never found in association with the feldspars proper. Minerals of the feldspathoid group are found in an unusual suite of igneous rocks that includes some syenites and rare gabbros. They weather quickly when on the Earth's surface and therefore do not survive very long in the sedimentary record.

Lazurite

(Na,Ca)$_8$(Al,Si)$_{12}$O$_{24}$(S,SO$_4$)
H. 5–5.5: S.G. 2.4
Cubic. Metamorphic rocks
Shades of blue. Blue streak. Dull glassy lustre. Small dodecahedral crystals are rare; usually found in large masses in metamorphosed limestones. Also known as lapis lazuli.

Leucite

KAlSi$_2$O$_6$
H. 5.5–6: S.G. 2.5
Cubic. Volcanic environments
Colourless, white or grey. White streak. Glassy lustre, transparent to translucent. Crystals usually trapezohedral; also occurs as disseminated grains. Uncommon, found in silica-poor lavas.

Nepheline

(Na,K)AlSiO$_4$
H. 5.5–6: S.G. 2.6
Hexagonal. Igneous rocks
White, grey, yellow, green, blue or red. White streak. Glassy lustre (greasy on cleavage surfaces). Transparent to opaque. Usually massive.

Sodalite

Na$_4$Al$_3$Si$_3$O$_{12}$Cl
H. 5.5–6: S.G. 2.3
Cubic. Igneous rocks
Normally blue, may be white, grey-pink, yellow or green. Streak white. Glassy lustre. Transparent to translucent. Crystals rare, usually found in large masses.

Zeolite group
Hydrated aluminosilicates
H. 3.5–5.5: S.G. 2.1–2.3
Various symmetries. Volcanic
rocks
A large group of closely-related minerals. Normally well crystallized. Transparent to translucent. Glassy lustre. White streak. Almost all occur in cavities in volcanic lavas. They are unusual in that they intumesce when heated (i.e. water is given off continously as the temperature is raised) and are named from the greek words for "boiling stone". Zeolites have a loose skeletal crystalline structure which enables them to selectively absorb molecules of a particular size; a recent use for them is in chemical purification systems and filters.

Natrolite
$Na_2Al_2Si_3O_{10}$. $2H_2O$
Orthorhombic
In the specimen shown, natrolite is the translucent mineral. Usually colourless or white, but can be shades of yellow, green or red. Crystals are usually needle-like and occur in radiating aggregates. One perfect cleavage. Brittle, with an uneven fracture.

Chabazite
$CaAl_2Si_4O_{12}$. $6H_2O$
Trigonal
White, yellow, pink (as here) or red in colour. Crystals resemble distorted cubes and often intergrow with one another. Chabazite has three poor cleavages parallel to the crystal faces.

Heulandite
$(Ca,Na_2)Al_2Si_7O_{18}$. $6H_2O$
Monoclinic
Colourless, white, grey, yellow, pink or brown. Occurs as tabular crystals that narrow slightly at their termination to make them resemble coffins. Often occurs in association with other zeolite minerals.

111

Scolecite

$CaAl_2Si_3O_{10}\cdot 3H_2O$
Monoclinic
Always colourless or white.
Transparent or translucent, with
a glassy or silky lustre. It is hard
but fragile, with perfect
cleavage. Crystals are prismatic,
but it is more often found in
fibrous, radiating masses that
curl up when heated. Most
frequently found in cavities in
basalt, but also occurs in cracks
in schists and contact-
metamorphosed limestones.

Stilbite

$NaCa_2Al_5Si_{13}O_{36}\cdot$
$16H_2O$
Monoclinic
Usually white or
yellow, but can
be reddish-brown.
Transparent to
translucent, with
a glassy to pearly
lustre. Twinned crystals
frequently form sheaf-like
aggregates. Occasionally found
as cruciform penetration twins.

Analcime

$NaAlSi_2O_6\cdot H_2O$
Cubic
Usually colourless or white,
sometimes greenish-grey, yellow
or pink. Unexpectedly light and
very fragile, with an uneven
fracture. No cleavage. Crystals
are normally trapezohedral or
modified cubes. Earthy, granular
or radiating fibrous masses also
occur. Sometimes found in
sedimentary rocks. Takes on a
small electrical charge when
rubbed or heated.

Layer silicates

These minerals are made up of extensive sheets of silica groups, usually giving them a perfect cleavage parallel to the direction of the sheets.

Chlorite group

$(Mg,Fe,Al)_6(Al,Si)_4O_{10}(OH)_8$
H. 2–2.5; S.G. 2.6–3.3
Monoclinic. Metamorphic rocks
A group of minerals with variable composition and complicated crystalline structure. Usually green in colour, but may be white, yellow, pink or brown. Streak white. Transparent to translucent. Dull glassy lustre. Crystals are rare; more frequently found as foliated, scaly masses with perfect basal cleavage, such as that seen in mica.

Chlorite minerals occur in a range of environments. They are alteration products formed by the weathering of micas and are often found in metamorphic rocks, to which they may impart a green colour.

Sometimes found in association with calcite, quartz and siderite; pictured here is chlorite coating siderite. Chlorite may be mistaken for talc, but is harder. It also resembles some micas, though it is rigid not flexible.

Kaolinite

$Al_2(Si_2O_5)(OH)_4$
H. 2–3; S.G. 2–2.7
Monoclinic. Beds of lakes and hydrothermal veins
Usually white, but can be tinted grey or yellow by trace impurities such as iron. It is rarely red, blue, brown or green. Streak is always white. Opaque, with a dull lustre that can be pearly on cleavage planes. Has one perfect cleavage. Crystals are invariably microscopic. Usually found as soft, earthy masses that have a chalky feel. When wet, it is pliable and slippery. Kaolinite forms from the weathering or alteration of feldspars and other aluminium silicates in near-surface sites. It forms large deposits in weathering granites.

Kaolinite is one of the most common clay minerals. All have similar physical properties, and form by the alteration of aluminium silicates. They are not readily distinguishable from each other in the field. Kaolinite is widely used in the ceramic and paper industries, and as a filler in paints and plastics.

Mica group

The mica minerals are all plate-like in habit, and flexible. They are common constituents of silica-rich igneous rocks, schists and slates.

Muscovite

$KAl_3Si_3O_{10}(OH)_2$
H.2.5–3: S.G. 2.8
Monoclinic. Igneous and metamorphic rocks
Sometimes called white mica. Commonly colourless or shades of grey, green, yellow or brown. Streak white. Dull glassy lustre. Crystals tabular, usually found in flaky or foliated masses which split easily along the cleavage plane into thin, flexible transparent or translucent sheets. Variety sericite occurs in large compact masses. A very common mineral in all granitic rocks, schists and gneisses.

Glauconite

$(K,Na)(Al,Fe^{3+},Mg)_2(Al,Si)_4O_{10}(OH)_2$
H: 2: S.G. 2.4–2.9
Monoclinic. Sedimentary rocks
Dull green in colour with a white streak. Opaque. Microscopic, lath-like crystals often found in fine-grained marine sedimentary rocks called "greensands".

Biotite

$K(Mg,Fe)_3(Al,Fe)Si_3O_{10}(OH,F)_2$
H. 2.5–3: S.G. 2.7–3.4
Monoclinic. Igneous and metamorphic rocks
Commonly black or dark shades of green or brown. Streak white. Glassy lustre. Crystals tabular, usually in flaky or foliated masses which split easily into thin, flexible transparent or translucent sheets.

Phlogopite

KMg₃AlSi₃O₁₀(OH)₂
$KMg_3AlSi_3O_{10}(OH)_2$
H. 2–3; S.G. 2.8
Monoclinic. Metamorphic rocks
Sometimes called bronze mica after its dark yellowy-brown colour. Streak white. Dull metallic lustre, transparent to translucent. Its six-sided crystals are sometimes referred to as "mica books". They split easily along the cleavage plane into thin flexible sheets. Found in dolomite marble.

Xanthophyllite

Ca₂(Mg₄.₆Al₁.₄)(Si₂.₅Al₅.₅O₂₀)(OH)₄
$Ca_2(Mg_{4.6}Al_{1.4})(Si_{2.5}Al_{5.5}O_{20})(OH)_4$
H. 3.5 on top, 6 on sides of crystal; S.G. 3
Monoclinic. Metamorphic rocks
Colourless, yellow, green, or reddish-brown. Streak white. Crystals are platy and show perfect cleavage parallel to their tops. Glassy lustre. Found in schists and skarns. An unusual mineral often confused with the other micas.

Lepidolite

K(Li,Al)₃(Si,Al)₄O₁₀(F,OH)₂
$K(Li,Al)_3(Si,Al)_4O_{10}(F,OH)_2$
H. 2.5–4; S.G. 2.8–3.3
Monoclinic. Pegmatites
Pink or pale purple, also white or shades of grey or yellow. Streak white. Dull glassy lustre.

Crystals tabular, usually found in flaky or foliated masses which split easily along the cleavage plane into thin, flexible transparent or translucent sheets.

Prehnite

Ca₂Al₂Si₃O₁₀(OH)₂
$Ca_2Al_2Si_3O_{10}(OH)_2$
H. 6–6.5: S.G. 2.9
Orthorhombic. Widespread occurrence

Usually a pale green colour, but can also be a deeper green, grey, colourless or white. Its colour tends to fade on prolonged exposure to light. Streak is always white. Translucent to transparent, with a glassy lustre. Crystals are most commonly tabular, and associate into aggregates. Also found in compact masses, which can be botryoidal, stalactitic or mamillary. Found as a secondary mineral in cavities in basalt, granite and gneiss, and in metamorphosed limestones and veins. Prehnite is sometimes confused with hemimorphite, though it is harder. Fine crystals are sometimes used as a gemstones.

Apophyllite

$KCa_4Si_8O_{20}(F,OH). 8H_2O$
H. 4.5–5: S.G. 2.4
Tetragonal. Igneous rocks

White or colourless, also pale shades of yellow or green. Streak white. Transparent to translucent crystals are almost cubic in form. The lustre is glassy on prism faces, which are also striated, but duller on the bases of the crystals. Occurs in cavities in basalt rocks, where it is usually associated with calcite, prehnite or members of the zeolite group. More rarely occurs in cavities in plutonic rocks.

Talc

$Mg_3Si_4O_{10}(OH)_2$
H. 1: S.G. 2.7
Monoclinic. Metamorphic rocks
White or green, with a white
streak. Greasy lustre, translucent
to opaque. Crystals are rare;
usually found as fine-grained
compact masses, which are often
referred to as "soapstone" or
"French chalk". Can be cut with
a knife. Formed as a result of
alteration of magnesium-rich
minerals such as olivine,
pyroxenes and amphiboles. Used
widely as a cosmetic and as a
filler in paper and paints.

Pyrophillite

$Al_2Si_4O_{10}(OH)_2$
H. 1–2: S.G. 2.6–2.9
Monoclinic.
Metamorphic rocks
White or shades of
yellow, green or brown.
Streak white. Dull glassy
lustre, translucent. Elongated
crystals are usually found in
foliated or radial masses. Cuts
with a knife. A very soft mineral,
similar to talc.

Chrysocolla

$CuSiO_3. 2H_2O$
H. 2–4: S.G. 2–2,4
Orthorhombic or monoclinic.
Hydrothermal veins
Blue-green in colour,
with a white to
turquoise streak. Very
dull glassy or earthy
lustre. Only found in
loosely-crystalline aggregates
that often form botryoidal
coatings. A secondary mineral
formed in the zone of
oxidation of copper veins.

Gemstones

Minerals and rocks have been used for decoration since early times. There is evidence that lapis lazuli was mined in Afghanistan over 6,000 years, ago and turquoise ornaments have been discovered in ancient Egyptian tombs. Polished stones were employed as lucky charms and medicines, and valued for their rarity and the status they gave the owner.

There is no rigid scientific definition of a gemstone. It can be said to be any mineral or rock that is perceived to have special value because of its combined attributes of beauty and rarity. Often inorganic, but sometimes derived from plants or animals, gems are usually durable and hold a polish well. Many gems are cut into facets, and for such stones the brilliant lustre and play of light from within the gem is the desirable attribute. For gems cut into the more simple *cabochon* – a circle or oval with a curved upper surface – it is the colour or play of colours, perhaps iridescence or cat's eye effect, that gives the stone its value. The most important characteristics of gems are discussed in this introductory section.

Although some gemstones have distinctive features that make their identification easy, for example diamond's extreme hardness, many are easily confused with one another. Although most gems are minerals, the destructive tests (such as streak and scratch) used to identify the latter cannot be applied to gems – it is profitless to find out how valuable your gem was before it was damaged. To identify stones with absolute certainty gemmologists use specialist equipment with which they observe the properties of light as it passes through the gem.

The problem of identification is compounded by the large number of very convincing imitation gems in circulation. Many of these are made of glass, which is much softer than most gem minerals and so is often chipped or scratched: moreover, glass stones may contain gas bubbles or have a "swirly" texture. Synthetic gems are quite different to imitations, being chemically identical to their naturally-occurring relatives. These stones are made in the laboratory by melting and mixing mineral ingredients, and letting this mass recrystallize under controlled conditions of temperature and pressure. Minute flaws introduced in the manufacturing process can sometimes reveal the true identity of synthetic stones: detecting these flaws requires requires expert equipment and knowledge.

Rarity

The rarer a gemstone, the greater its commercial value. Some gems are rare varieties of common minerals. Quartz, for instance, is one of the most common minerals in the Earth's crust, but its gem varieties, such as amethyst and citrine are rare, being unusual in their colour and clarity. Other gem minerals are extremely rare: diamonds, for example, account for perhaps 5 grammes of every 100 tonnes of their host rock.

Large gem specimens occur less frequently than small stones and are considerably more valuable. Gems are weighed in carats, with one carat equivalent to 0.2 grammes. Carats themselves are subdivided into points, and there are 100 points to a carat. On this kind of scale some of the famous gems are incredibly large. The Cullinan diamond found in South Africa in 1905, weighed 3,106 carats in its rough state. It was cut into nine large stones, the heaviest of these weighing 530 carats, and over 100 smaller stones. An aquamarine of cuttable quality, found in Brazil in 1910, weighed a staggering 110.5 kg, which is 552,500 carats!

Hardness and durability

Most dust contains minute particles of of quartz, which has a hardness of 7 on Mohs' scale (see p. 29). In day-to-day wear, gems are constantly exposed to dust, so most minerals used as gems are harder than quartz and therefore cannot be scratched by it. Diamond is the hardest of all minerals, scoring 10 on Mohs' scale. Ruby and sapphire rate a hardness of 9, topaz and spinel both have a hardness of 8. Some gems, like amber and fluorite are much softer, and are valued for the ease with which they can be carved.

Hardness alone is not enough to make a long-lasting gem. Emerald is very brittle, so despite its hardness it fractures easily. Diamond has well developed cleavage – planes of weakness. This limits the ways in which gems can be faceted and makes poorly-cut stones prone to breakage. Two of the toughest gemstones are the jade minerals – jadeite and nephrite. Although they have hardnesses of between 6 and 7 they are as resistant to breaking as hardened steel. This property makes them particularly suitable for carving.

Gems and light

White light is made up of many different colours, each colour having a different wavelength. Blue light, for example, has a shorter wavelength than red light. As white light passes through a gem, certain wavelengths may be filtered out: those that survive passage give the stone its colour. Sometimes it is an element essential to the mineral's composition that blocks the passage of certain wavelengths and gives the gem its colour. But more often, trace impurities – such as iron and chromium – or irregularities in crystal structure act as the "filter" and determine colour. However colour arises, it is of great importance in determining the value and desirability of a stone. Some gems can have their colour altered or improved by heating or irradiation. For example, the depth of colour of pale aquamarines is frequently improved by heat treatment.

Sometimes the interaction of light with a gemstone produces not a single colour but several. Gems like diamond have the capacity to separate out the different wavelengths as light passes through them, so that glints of many colours are produced. This property, known as dispersion, gives diamonds their "fire". Some minerals have regularly-spaced spheres or planes of minerals in their structure, which interfere with the passage of certain wavelengths of light through the gem. Some colours survive passage, but others are filtered out. This interference produces iridescence and play a of colours, such as that observed in precious opal.

White light can be differently "filtered" along different axes of a crystal. This effect can be quite profound: rubies and sapphires vary in colour intensity with the direction in which they are viewed; alexandrite, the extreme example, changes colour from green to red according to the direction of viewing. This phenomenon is known as pleochroism.

If an object is half immersed in water, it appears bent at the water surface. This is because light is slowed down and bent (or refracted) as it passes from water to air. Light is also refracted when it crosses the boundary between air and a gem. Most gem minerals are singly refractive, i.e., they bend light through one angle only. Doubly refractive minerals – such as calcite and the olivine gem, peridot – bend light through two distinct angles, so objects viewed through these minerals appear double.

The way in which light reacts with the surface of a gem is known as lustre (see p. 29). Most gem minerals have a glassy or resinous lustre, which is considered to be more desirable than a dull or earthy appearance.

Finally, impurities and tiny inclusions in the mineral can form sets of parallel fibres which cause cat's eye or star effects within the mineral.

Cutting and polishing

The famous Timur ruby is inscribed with the names of several of its previous owners, including that of the fearsome Timur himself. Inscription is the first way in which gems were decorated. Polishing of cleavage planes and crystal faces to make them more transparent and lustrous was probably the next form of embellishment to become widespread. Another early technique was cutting stones into *cabochons*. This cut is still widely used, particularly for opaque gems.

Faceted cuts are the most highly developed style of gem presentation and are thought to have developed in the 15th century. They are used for gems of high transparency and smooth, even colour. These cuts display lustre and fire to their best advantage, the back facets acting like mirrors to reflect light through the top of the gem. Many variations of faceted cuts have been developed, all of which need enormous care and skill to execute successfully.

The major gemstone groups

Most gemstones can be loosely assigned to groups, the members of which have similar chemical compositions or are of similar origin.

Beryl group All are beryllium aluminium silicate minerals. Gem quality beryl is transparent and usually cut into facets, though it lacks the fire and high lustre of diamond. It is brittle, but without cleavage. Its colour is highly variable since it is imparted by trace impurities. Many varieties can be artificially synthesized.

Chrysoberyl group There are three varieties of precious chrysoberyl – cymophane, alexandrite and chrysoberyl itself. All are beryllium aluminium oxide minerals. Colour is variable and comes from trace impurities of chromium.

Corundum group The two gem varieties of corundum – ruby and sapphire – are aluminium oxide minerals. Pure corundum is colourless; gem quality stones are coloured by impurities and are strongly pleochroic. Corundum is the hardest mineral after diamond, though it is brittle. It is cut both in facets and *en cabochon*. Faceted stones have a high lustre, while *cabochons* can show a silky sheen, cat's eye or star effects caused by inclusions of other minerals.

Feldspar group These gems are all calcium, sodium or potassium aluminium silicate minerals. Their value comes from the unusual optical effects they often display. Feldspars are relatively soft for gems and can be scratched by household dust. They are most commonly cut *en cabochon*.

Garnet group The garnet gems are complex silicate minerals. They occur in a variety of colours, but are always translucent or transparent. They can be cut into facets, *en cabochon*, or carved into cameos or small objects.

Organic gems These gems come from the remains of animals or plants, either recently dead or fossilized. They are less dense and softer than most other gemstones, with harnesses not exceeding 4, and specific gravities ranging from 1.04 (amber) to 2.78 (pearl).

Quartz group Quartz is one of the most common minerals in the crust of the Earth. It has gem varieties that are both crystalline and amorphous. It is coloured by trace impurities or defects in its crystal structure. Quartz is relatively soft for a gemstone, and is cut both *en cabachon* and faceted.

Rocks as gems Several rocks are of great ornamental value. They are commonly carved or cut for use in jewellery.

The best-known gemstones are described and illustrated on the following pages. Each is shown in both uncut and cut form, and its distinctive features are listed. Most of the gemstones described here also appear in the **Rocks** or **Minerals** sections of the book. These entries are cross-referenced, and should be consulted for a fuller account of the gems' physical properties – such as streak, specific gravity and hardness.

Emerald

This beryl gem's characteristic green colour is imparted by minute quantities of chromium and sometimes vanadium. Tiny inclusions of other minerals distinguish true emeralds from synthetic gems. These inclusions often make emeralds cloudy. (See beryl, page 96).

Aquamarine

This beryl gem varies from light to dark blue in colour. Dark stones are more valuable, so the light ones are sometimes heated to darken them. They are coloured by iron. Inclusions and growth lines are common. (See beryl, p. 96).

Golden beryl

The colour of this gemstone varies from lemon yellow to golden yellow, and is caused by traces of iron. It is transparent and rarely contains visible impurities. When heated to temperatures above 250° C, golden beryl permanently loses its colour. (See beryl, p. 96).

Morganite

This pink to violet variety of beryl is transparent and cut into facets. In some instances, colour can be improved by heating the gems to over 400° C. Traces of manganese produce this gem's colour. (See beryl, p. 96).

Chrysoberyl

Varies in colour from golden yellow to green or brown. It is transparent with an exceedingly high lustre, and is cut into faceted gems. Pale yellow stones were particularly prized in the 18th century. (See chrysoberyl, p. 62).

Cymophane

Also known as chrysoberyl cat's eye. Parallel hollow tubular inclusions give a strong cat's eye effect; stones are cut *en cabochon* to emphasize this property. Cymophane is the greek word Greek for "waving light". (See chrysoberyl, p. 62).

Alexandrite
Under natural light, this chrysoberyl variety appears green, but in artificial light it turns red. It is cut in facets. Looked at from different angles, the same gem will appear red, orange-yellow and green. This is known as pleochroism. (See chrysoberyl, p.62).

Ruby
Ruby is red corundum. It is always coloured by chrome, and sometimes by iron. The most valuable types are red with a hint of blue, a colour known as pigeon's blood. When powdered, ruby is used as an industrial abrasive. (See corundum, p. 68).

Sapphire
This corundum variety is usually blue, but can also be pink, orange, green, purple or black. Iron, titanium and chromium produce the variation of colour. There is a complete gradation of colour between ruby and sapphire. (See corundum, p. 68).

Labradorite

This plagioclase feldspar is characterized by a brilliant blue and green iridescence. This is caused by the effect of light on closely-spaced planes within the stone. Labradorite cameos are sometimes produced. (See plagioclase feldspars, p.108).

Amazonite

This gemstone is a variety of microcline. Its green or blue-green colour is caused by the presence of lead and water impurities. It is opaque, often with a streaked texture rather like finely-woven cloth. (See potash feldspars, p. 107).

Moonstone

The gem variety of adularia. It is transparent in colour but with a blue-white sheen on its surface. Sometimes it shows cat's eye effects caused by finely-spaced sheets of silica within the stone. (See potash feldspars, p. 107).

Blue john

This fluorite gem is banded purple, white and yellow. Large
deposits, such as those in Derbyshire (UK) and Saxony (Germany)
have been extensively mined for many centuries. Massive blocks
were often carved into vases and bowls. (See fluorite, p. 59)

Green fluorite

Fluorite is a common, cubic mineral often found in hydrothermal
veins. It is usually purple or blue. Green fluorite, cut into facets or
en cabochon, is an unusual, but rather soft (hardness 4) gem. (See
fluorite, p.59).

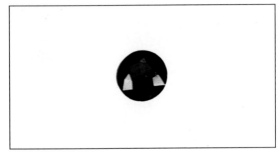

Almandine

The most abundant of the garnet gems. Good quality stones are red
with a hint of violet; colour is produced by iron, which is a
necessary part of the chemical composition. Usually faceted, but
sometimes cut *en cabochon*. (See garnet group, p.90)

Pyrope

Named from the Greek word for "fire", this garnet variety is red with a brownish tint. Traces of chromium produce this colouration. When a deep red colour, it is sometimes called ruby. It was very fashionable in the 18th and 19th centuries. (See garnet group, p. 90).

Hessonite

This member of the garnet group is a calcium aluminium silicate. It is orange, coloured by traces of iron impurities. Hessonite is sometimes known as cinnamon-stone. (See garnet group, p.90).

Demantoid

This valuable garnet gem is a calcium iron silicate. It is very rare and has a vivid green colour produced by traces of chromium. High dispersion (separation of white light into colours) and refractive index make this a spectacular, fiery gem. (See garnet group, p. 90).

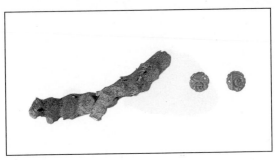

Coral
An organic gem composed of calcium carbonate secreted by tiny colonial invertebrates. Black, pink and white are the most common colours; all varieties are opaque and are usually cut *en cabochon* or carved. Polished coral has a glassy lustre.

Pearl
These organic gems are also composed of calcium carbonate secreted by some molluscs, especially oysters. They are usually cream or white but can be grey, black, pink or blue. They are translucent to opaque with a characteristically pearly lustre.

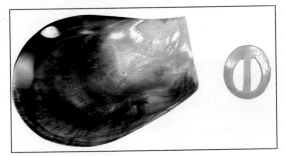

Mother of pearl
Has the same chemical composition as pearl. It is deposited by molluscs on to the inside of their shells. It is much more common than pearl and consequently much less valuable.

Jet

Fossilized wood that has been turned into a dense form of lignite coal. Dark brown or black in colour, it is opaque with a velvety lustre. It can hold a high polish and is usually made into beads, carvings or cameos. (See lignite, p.24).

Amber

This organic gem is fossilized tree resin, usually about 50 million years old. It is typically orange, but varies from yellow through red to brown. It is transparent to opaque and can contain the preserved remains of insects and even small vertebrates, such as lizards.

Rock crystal

This colourless and transparent variety of quartz has a glassy lustre, is very brittle and fractures easily. It is cut into facets and *cabochons*. Rock crystal is the pure form of quartz, without impurities or defects. (See quartz group, p. 102)

Smoky quartz

Varies from dark brown to smoky grey, the colour being produced by aluminium impurities. It is tough but very brittle, and is frequently carved into bowls, which shatter if hit. This gem often contains gas bubbles or solid inclusions. (See quartz group, p. 102).

Citrine

This quartz gemstone is coloured yellow to orange-brown. It is transparent and is normally cut into facets. Natural citrine is rare, but it can be formed artificially by heating amethyst or smoky quartz. (See quartz group, p.102).

Cairngorm

A variety of smoky quartz from Mt. Cairngorm (Scotland, UK). Much used locally as an ornamental stone. (See quartz group, p. 102).

Amethyst

A purple to pale violet, frequently colour-banded, form of quartz. The colour is due to iron oxide impurities and natural irradiation. It is transparent and very brittle, and cut both *en cabochon* and into faceted gems. (See quartz group, p. 102).

Tiger's eye

This quartz gem is golden yellow, warm brown or black with a silky lustre, and is cut *en cabochon*. It is formed by the replacement of an asbestiform variety of riebeckite, by quartz. Remains of the riebeckite give the mineral its colour. (See quartz group, p. 102).

Prase

A leek-green aggregate of quartz crystals. It is full of inclusions of the mineral actinolite, which give it a mottled, sparkling appearance. Prase can easily be mistaken for nephrite (a form of jade). (See quartz group, p. 102).

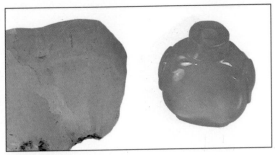

Chalcedony

A microcrystalline variety of quartz. It is less brittle than large crystals (such as smoky quartz) and has a waxy lustre. Chalcedony is built up from thin layers of quartz, which often vary in colour. It is commonly cut into *cabochons*. (See quartz group, p.102).

Carnelian

This variety of chalcedony is often cherry-red, but may be brownish. It is dull but transparent, with a cloudy distribution of colour caused by iron oxide impurities. Colour may be enhanced by dyeing with iron salts. (See quartz group, p. 102).

Bloodstone

Also known as heliotrope. A mottled green and red opaque variety of chalcedony. The red spots it contains were once thought to be made from Christ's blood and the stone was much used in in carvings depicting religious scenes. (See quartz group, p. 102).

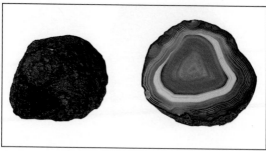

Agate
A banded variety of chalcedony, which may be translucent or opaque. It forms in cavities in eruptive rocks. Colour variation of the bands of iron oxide within the quartz determines the stone's value. Often stained. (See quartz group, p. 102).

Moss agate
This form of chalcedony is generally colourless and contains tree-like growths or random tangles of green minerals – most frequently hornblende. Technically these stones should not be called agates, since they lack banding. (See quartz group, p. 102).

Onyx
A variety of agate in which white bands alternate with black, brown or red bands. It is translucent or opaque with a waxy lustre and is often used for cameo carving. (See quartz group, p. 102).

Jasper

A fairly common, spotted form of chalcedony. It occurs in a variety of colours, most often red, brown or black. This opaque stone is usually coloured by iron oxides, but occasionally by clay minerals or by goethite. (See quartz group, p. 102).

Opal

One of the most valuable forms of quartz. It contains water in its structure, and the quartz is formed into microscopically small spheres, packed close together. Precious opal reflects a play of colours, most often blues and reds. (See quartz group, p. 102).

Obsidian

This fine-grained, silica-rich igneous rock is opaque and generally black, but can also be grey, brown or green. It sometimes contains amorphous white spots formed by microscopic aggregates of minerals – this variety is known as snowflake obsidian.

Serpentine

An altered, silica-poor igneous rock. It is green or yellow, sometimes with streaks of white and black. There is often a mixture of colours in a patchy snakeskin texture. It is tough and usually opaque. Carvings and *cabochon* cut jewels are common.

Nephrite

Also called jade (together with jadeite). This gem is made up of fine-grained aggregates of crystals, and is most valuable when green, but can also be white, yellow, red or brown. It is usually spotted or contains irregular blotches of colour. (See nephrite, p. 99).

Kunzite

This gem is a pale pink to light violet form of spodumene; it can become faded with time. Brown and green varieties also occur, the colour of which may be improved by heating. Kunzite is always cut into facets. (See pyroxene group, p. 100).

Diamond

The hardest known mineral. It is graded according to the "four Cs" – colour, clarity, cut and carat weight. Gem diamonds are transparent and may be colourless, yellow, green, red, brown or black. Value is reduced by inclusions and flaws. (See diamond, p. 44).

Hematite

Thin plates of hematite are red and transparent. The form more commonly used for jewellery is specular hematite, which is black and opaque with a brilliant lustre. Its name comes from the Greek word "blood", in allusion to its red colour.

Hematite

This stone is most often cut into beads, and *cabochons* and faceted stones are also produced. Though not as hard as many other gems, and fairly easily scratched, its use as a decorative stone is increasing. (See hematite, p. 61).

Lapis lazuli

An opaque and intensely blue gem. It polishes to a glassy lustre and often has a grainy texture, with frequent spots and streaks of white calcite and gold pyrite. Plain blue lapis is the most valuable and comes only from Afghanistan. (See feldspathoid group, p. 110).

Malachite

Gems are microscopic crystalline aggregates. They are light or emerald green to black in colour, and usually banded. Malachite is opaque and polishes to a silky lustre. It is cut *en cabochon* or into beads, and is frequently carved (See malachite, p. 69).

Spinel

Highly variable in colour, spinel may be pink, violet, orange, red, blue, dark green and black. It is usually transparent with a brilliant lustre. This mineral is similar in composition to ruby; many famous rubies have been found to be red spinels. (See spinel, p. 67).

Topaz

This gemstone is transparent and usually pale in colour. Yellow, reddish-brown, light blue, pink, pale green and colourless forms occur. Colour can be changed by heating. This hard gemstone is usually faceted. (See topaz, p. 92).

Tourmaline

Highly variable in colour; pink and green varieties are most valuable. It is usually transparent, but the black form (called schorl) is opaque. The lustre is glassy. Coloured stones have a more intense hue when viewed from the top. (See tourmaline group, p. 95).

Turquoise

The colour of this gemstone varies from sky blue through green-blue to green. It is opaque and has a waxy lustre when polished. The sky blue form is the most valuable; the colour comes from the essential copper in the mineral. (See turquoise, p. 80).

Zircon
Variably coloured, this gemstone is most commonly yellow, brown, green, blue or colourless. It is transparent or translucent, with a diamond-like fire and lustre. Almost invariably cut into facets. All but green stones show strong double refraction. (See zircon, p. 92).

Glossary

Accessory mineral   A mineral present in an igneous rock in small amounts, such that its presence or absence does not affect the classification of that rock.

Adamantine   A brilliant, shiny lustre.

Asbestos   A fibrous form of several minerals, most of which are amphiboles.

Bedding   A surface of deposition which is usually planar, separating two rock types of sedimentary origin.

Clast   Fragment of mineral or preexisting rock incorporated into a sediment.

Cleavage   Regular planes of weakness in a mineral. Their position is determined by crystal structure. Also used to describe planes of weakness in metamorphic rocks.

Cockscomb crystals   Aggregates of bladed crystals that resemble a cockscomb.

Conchoidal fracture   A fracture pattern of concentric circles in a curved surface. Seen in glasses and some minerals.

Concretionary   Mineral growth after burial of a sediment, through the accumulation of compounds into small areas of the rock. The resulting growths have varied shapes and sizes.

Country rock   The rock surrounding an igneous intrusion or hydrothermal vein.

Cross-bedding   A wave-like shape to bedding.

Dispersion   The splitting of light into its component colours.

Dykes   Planar bodies of igneous (and occasionally sedimentary) rock which cut across the bedding of the surrounding rocks.

Equant   Crystals that have the same length in all directions.

Fissile   A thin-bedded or cleaved rock that splits easily along planes of weakness.

Foliated   Rocks that bear parallel-orientated platy minerals, developed as a result of metamorphism.

Geode   A cavity lined with inward-pointing crystals

Gradational   A gradual change from one state to another, sometimes from one mineral to another, or from one rock type to another. Within sediments, this term refers to changes in clast size from coarser to finer.

Greensands   Sandstones coloured green by the mineral glauconite.

High grade metamorphism   Metamorphism at high temperatures and pressures.

High level intrusions   Igneous rock bodies that have crystallized close to the surface of the Earth.

Hydrothermal veins   Mineral veins deposited from heated water ejected from an igneous intrusion.

Imbrication   Directional stacking of clasts in a sedimentary rock.

Intergrown   An intimate association of two or more minerals that have formed simultaneously.

Intrusive contact   The contact between an intrusion and the rock it has cut in its entry into the area.

Lath-like   A platy form of minerals.

Low grade metamorphism   Metamorphism at low temperatures and pressures.

Low level intrusions   Igneous rocks that have crystallized deep in the crust of the Earth.

Magma   Molten rock generated inside the crust or upper mantle of the Earth.

Mammilary   Breast-shaped habit of minerals.

Micaceous   Mica bearing, or with a platy appearance reminiscent of mica.

Placers   Sedimentary accumulations of heavy, valuable minerals.

Plutons   Deep-seated igneous rocks of large volume.

Secondary mineral   A mineral formed by the metamorphism of a preexisting mineral.

Siliceous   Silica-rich rock.

Sills   Planar bodies of igneous rock that intrude parallel to the bedding of the surrounding rock.

Slump deposit   Sediment produced by the abrupt failure of a slope, usually on land, but occasionally in the sea.

Solid solution series   A set of minerals of similar composition. They share elements, but possess them in varying amounts.

Twinned   Sets of crystals that are structurally related to each other and grow together in a regular manner.

Zone of alteration   A region where a mineral is subjected to a different set of conditions to those under which it originally formed, causing it to be replaced by another mineral that is stable under the new conditions.

Index